GOLD
FOR THE
GODS

Exhibition dates

Royal Ontario Museum, Toronto
September 28 — November 21, 1976

Winnipeg Art Gallery
December 17, 1976 — February 20, 1977

Montreal Museum of Fine Arts
March 18 — May 15, 1977

GOLD FOR THE GODS

a catalogue to
an exhibition of pre-Inca and Inca gold and artifacts from Peru
by
A. D. TUSHINGHAM

with contributions by
Kent C. Day, Royal Ontario Museum
and
Léo Rosshandler, Montreal Museum of Fine Arts

Colour photography by
Leighton Warren, Royal Ontario Museum
and
Fritz Mandl, Museum für Völkerkunde, Vienna

ROM
Royal Ontario Museum

Copyright © 1976 by the
Royal Ontario Museum
ISBN 0-88854-187-2

Cover illustration: Poncho (136)
Page 2: Mask (220)

Publication of this catalogue was assisted
by a subvention from the Canada Council.

Catalogue design by Michael Clasby Ltd.

Maps on pp. 25, 31, 35, 41 and 49 and
drawings on pages 29 and 33 by
David Findlay

Drawings on p. 135 by Julian Mulock

Typesetting by Fleet Typographers Ltd.

Printing (b & w) and binding by the
Hunter Rose Co. Ltd.

Colour printing by
Herzig Somerville Ltd.

Printed and bound in Canada

GOLD FOR THE GODS

an exhibition of Pre-Inca and Inca gold and artifacts lent by the Government of Peru to the Government of Canada, through its Ambassadors in Peru and Finland.

The exhibition has been organized by the Royal Ontario Museum, Toronto.

The objects are lent by the Mujica Gallo Foundation and the Museo Oro del Peru through the courtesy of Sr. Miguel Mujica Gallo.

Official authorization for the temporary export of the material was granted by Division General of the Army, President Francisco Morales Bermudez C. in Supreme Resolution no. 0010-76-ED of June 1, 1976 on the recommendation of the Peruvian Minister of Education and the Director General of the National Institute of Culture.

We wish to express our deep appreciation for the support and assistance afforded by the above-named officials and by many others, in Peru and Canada, who have contributed their efforts towards making the exhibition a success.

ORO PARA LOS DIOSES

Una exhibición de objetos de oro y otros objetos pre-hispánicos de las épocas pre-incaicas e incaica prestados por el Gobierno del Perú al Gobierno de Canadá a través de sus embajadores en el Perú y en Finlandia.

Organizado por el Royal Ontario Museum, Toronto.

Los objetos han sido prestados por la Fundación Mujica Gallo y el Museo Oro del Perú gracias a la cortesía del Sr. Miguel Mujica Gallo.

La autorización oficial para exportación temporal de estos objetos fue otorgada por el General de Division EP, Presidente Francisco Morales Bermudez C., de acuerdo a la Resolución Suprema no. 0010-76-ED del 1º de junio de 1,976, con la aprobación del Ministerio de Educación del Perú y del Director General del Instituto Nacional de Cultura del Perú.

Deseamos expresarles nuestros más sinceros agradecimientos por la ayuda que nos han prestado las autoridades mencionadas más arriba, y otras autoridades en el Perú y Canadá, quienes con su esfuerzo han contribuido para que esta exhibición sea un éxito.

James E. Cruise, Director
Gordon D. Wotherspoon, Chairman
Royal Ontario Museum

Roger L. Selby, Director
A. S. Leach, Jr., President
Winnipeg Art Gallery

David G. Carter, Director
Sean B. Murphy, President
Montreal Museum of Fine Arts

Contents

Foreword

For the first time, a large selection of objects from the Museo "Oro del Peru" is being exhibited in Canada. This exhibition, in Toronto, Montreal, and Winnipeg, contains the largest number of pieces ever shown together outside Lima; many, in fact, have never before left Peru. It is a pleasure for me to have the opportunity to introduce, through this series of exhibitions, something of the rich cultural heritage of ancient Peru.

I established the Museo "Oro del Peru" in 1966 in order to put my collection of ancient Peruvian gold, silver, and copper objects, along with featherwork, textiles, and jewellery, on public display for the enjoyment of visitors to Lima. The collection of objects began, however, in the 1930s when it came to my attention that richly stocked tombs in the northern part of the country were being systematically looted. In order to preserve these treasures for Peru, I began purchasing some of the more important pieces. As time has gone by, I have continued to collect objects made of precious metals or decorated with precious metals. All of these materials were deposited in the Museo "Oro del Peru" and are now officially registered as part of the national patrimony of Peru.

Over the past ten years exhibitions of objects from this collection have been shown in Mexico, South America, the United States, and Europe. However, none of these previous exhibitions reached Canada. I am delighted that such a fine representation of the ancient arts and crafts of Peru will now be presented to the Canadian public.

I hope the Canadian people will enjoy viewing this exhibition and, through it, come to know more of the heritage of Peru and the accomplishments of the ancient Peruvians.

Miguel Mujica Gallo
Lima
July 1, 1976

Introduction
A. D. Tushingham

The original suggestion that a Canadian exhibition of pre-Columbian gold was long overdue came from Mrs. H. Downie, Exhibition and Programme Officer for the Royal Ontario Museum. Dr. Kent C. Day, the ROM's archaeologist in Peru, Dr. David M. Pendergast, the head of our field work in Latin America, and I discussed the matter with her and studied the catalogues of exhibitions already held. Finally, it was decided to have a Peruvian gold exhibition if we could supplement the material from the Museo "Oro del Peru", already seen abroad, with an additional loan from the same famous collection.

To discover whether that would be possible, I joined Dr. Day in Peru in April 1975. Together we discussed the matter with Don Miguel Mujica Gallo, the man whose investment of concern and money saved so much of this valuable material for his native land; with his representative, Sr. Augusto Bouroncle; and with Mr. Robert Booth, the Project Director in South America of Tourism Investments S.A., which had been entrusted with the handling of all administrative matters by Don Miguel. Last, but not least, we discussed our hopes with officials of the Cultural Affairs division of the Department of External Affairs in Ottawa, particularly with Mr. Freeman Tovell, Mr. Jacques Asselin, and Miss Réjane Dodd, and with the Canadian Ambassador to Peru, Mr. Pierre Trottier, and his Second Secretary, Mr. David Brisco. Inevitably, a loan exhibition of this scale and quality would be negotiated at a very high diplomatic level, and we wished to follow the accepted channels of communication. That our concern for proper attention to diplomatic channels was justified has been amply demonstrated by the support provided by our government and its representatives — not only those just mentioned but also Mr. Paul Malone, the Canadian Ambassador to Finland, who acted on our behalf in the transmission to Canada of that part of the exhibition which has been circulating in Europe.

Don Miguel's personal enthusiasm for the idea of a Canadian exhibition was decisive and enabled us to proceed immediately to a selection of those objects in the collection that we thought would best complement the large exhibition already scheduled for Europe in the autumn of 1975 and the spring of 1976, and thereafter available for the Canadian tour. Dr. Day and I sought to select objects which had never before been seen outside of Peru and which had an intrinsic interest or importance transcending mere costliness. In this category the back-rest from a royal litter (237) must take precedence. It is not only a magnificent work in itself, but the little figures so carefully caparisoned in gold masks, headdresses, and breastplates, grasping staffs and cups (?), and standing in hieratic triads within an architectural framework, make it a prime historic document of the Chimu period. Because of this back-rest, the full-scale objects in gold elsewhere in the exhibition, often showing traces of paint, can be related to one another and can be dated in a far more dependable way than would otherwise be possible.

To further illustrate the pattern of our choice, we selected the funerary group (250), not only because it showed what a complete litter looked like but also because it allowed us to draw inferences about the appurtenances of everyday life in the early Chimu period and the views held about the after-life. The doll (129), the child's boots (248, 249), and the little poncho (238) afforded happy glimpses into family life, while the beautifully woven poncho decorated with gold (247), the head-band and sash (240 and 132), the caps (239, 133), and the feather headdresses (127, 128, 252) allowed us to visualize how an adult of the upper classes might have been clothed. On the other hand, the breastplates (364,365) were chosen just because they were so exotic, so unlike anything else we knew from Peru.

Even while making this original selection, we were thinking of another possibility: a symposium on pre-Columbian metallurgy. There has been a great deal of guesswork about the methods of extracting ore and of working metal in America before the arrival of the Europeans. Much of the uncertainty has been removed by recent studies and publications, but we felt that there were many problems still uninvestigated which could possibly be solved if some of the new material we were selecting could be subjected to a variety of non-destructive tests by a panel of experts. Don Miguel was excited by the prospect of discovering answers to the many outstanding problems; he generously gave us full permission to carry out whatever tests were necessary and even arranged for the shipment of the supplementary collection to Canada several months in advance of the opening of the exhibition to allow the scientists the opportunity to carry out their researches at their comparative leisure. Unfortunately, because of the necessity of sending this catalogue to press before the symposium is held, the new discoveries and insights must be published separately. Nonetheless, we are happy to acknowledge here the enthusiastic support of The Birks Family Foundation expressed in its financing of the symposium itself and of the publication of the results.

In response to Don Miguel's acceptance of our overtures, I returned to Toronto for consultations with Mrs. Downie and with the intention of interesting other Canadian institutions in sharing with the Royal Ontario Museum this wonderful opportunity. Not only did the Winnipeg Art Gallery and the Montreal Museum of Fine Arts join forces with us, but Mr. Léo Rosshandler, the Deputy Director of the Montreal Museum, was persuaded to write a section of the catalogue on the significance of gold for the ancient Peruvian peoples. This contribution complemented beautifully the factual and scientific resumés of the succession of Peruvian cultures and of the Peruvian achievements in the realm of metallurgy.

Fortified by such interest and support, a small party assembled in Lima during November 1975 to make the final arrangements. Mrs. Izabella Block-Bolten, a specialist in textile conservation, was loaned by Mr. Bernard Leech, Associate Curator-in-charge of the ROM's Conservation Department, to study the textiles and assess their condition; in fact, she went far beyond this simple (!) commission to provide a great deal of information on the condition of many other objects, facts which were often decisive in our choice of pieces for the exhibition. Mr. Leighton Warren, the Museum's head photographer, was on hand to photograph all objects

chosen for the supplementary list. Mrs. Downie handled an endless number of "political" and diplomatic matters, investigated the possibility of selling Peruvian arts and crafts as an adjunct of the exhibition, dealt with the minutiae of contracts, set up meetings with Peruvian officials, kept our own Embassy staff informed of our activities, and also managed all our financial affairs. Dr. Day came down from our archaeological dig near Chiclayo to assist in the final selection of the supplementary list and in the description of some of the pieces. He and Mrs. Downie worked at translating the Spanish descriptions that appeared on the registry sheets of the objects in the European travelling exhibition, to provide the information for our own catalogue of that material. Mr. and Mrs. Rosshandler joined us for a few days for profitable discussions, and particularly to outline the several responsibilities of Day, Rosshandler, and myself for the preparation of the catalogue.

When the study was completed, a mass of material was available which had to be collated and prepared for the Museum's Supervisor of Publications, Mr. John Campsie. The production of the French edition of the catalogue required the experienced assistance of the Montreal Museum of Fine Arts, specifically of Mr. Bill Bantey and of Mme. Françoise Saint-Michel who super-

13

vised the translation from the English edition, and of Mmes. Jacqueline Primeau and Camille Letourneau who edited the French version. We also acknowledge with thanks the contribution made by the Canada Council towards the cost of publishing the catalogue. We should also like to thank Dr. Hans Mandorff, Director of the Museum für Völkerkunde in Vienna, Dr. Peter Kann, keeper of the American collections, and Herr Fritz Mandl, chief photographer of that fine institution, for their assistance in preparing this catalogue.

Throughout, our assessment of what could constitute a significant display of Peruvian art in gold has had the blessing and the encouragement of the Museum's former Director, Dr. Walter Tovell, its present Director, Dr. James E. Cruise, the Chairman of the Board, Mr. Gordon Wotherspoon, and the Board itself. We are happy to acknowledge their support, and also to recognize the interest of Mr. Roger Selby, Director, and the Board of the Winnipeg Art Gallery, and of Mr. David G. Carter, Director, and the Board of the Montreal Museum of Fine Arts, without whose collaboration this fine exhibition could never have come to Canada.

To the members of the staff of the Museo "Oro del Peru" in Lima, and particularly to Sr. Augusto Bouroncle, who has at every turn demonstrated his interest in the exhibition and his concern for the wellbeing of the Canadian party working in Peru, we offer our appreciation of their constant help. To Mr. Robert Booth, the Project Director of Tourism Investments S.A. in South America, we tender our thanks for assistance in solving many administrative and communication difficulties (especially when a long postal strike in Canada threatened to bring all planning to a halt).

Finally, to Don Miguel Mujica Gallo himself, the head of the Foundation which now holds these golden treasures in trust for the people of Peru, we extend our heartfelt gratitude for warm friendship and for the enthusiasm with which he greeted our request for a Canadian tour of his world-famous collection. We trust that our exhibition and catalogue will make Canadians more aware of the high achievements of our predecessors in the Americas before the coming of the Europeans, none of which exceed, in imagination and performance, the best products of Peru's ancient craftsmen in gold, ceramics, textiles, and architecture.

The Meaning of Gold to the Ancient Peruvians

Léo Rosshandler

The present exhibition is a reflection of historic events which occurred on November 16, 1532, in Cajamarca, a small town in northern Peru that at the time was an Inca stronghold. Here, as fate decreed, took place the tragic encounter between Francisco Pizarro, leader of a band of treasure-hungry Spanish adventurers, and the Inca Atahualpa, king and master of an empire bursting with riches. The Inca, who was over-confident because of his recent victory in a bloody war of succession, fell into the trap laid by the Spaniards. "The king, surrounded by 25,000 Indians, marched on the square of Cajamarca, where the Spanish had prepared an ambush. He was carried in triumph, adorned with golden jewellery, and multi-coloured feathers."[1] According to the chroniclers, the noblemen who accompanied him also wore ornaments of gold and silver. Atahualpa was taken prisoner and his escort massacred.

The following day in Cajamarca the Inca's palace and property were sacked. "Countless objects in gold and silver, jewellery as well as ornaments, were stolen."[2] Atahualpa could not remain unaware of the intentions of the Spanish: they were after gold. How bizarre such an attitude seemed to him is demonstrated by the account, given by one of the chroniclers, of how pleased Atahualpa was with some glass beads shown him by the Span-iards. "I am astonished," he told Pizarro, "that you roam the world in search of metals as common as gold and silver when in Castile things as beautiful as these can be found."[3] These words, spoken by the Inca Atahualpa to his jailer and executioner shortly before his death, show that the value and role of gold were understood very differently by the Incas and the Spanish. It also sets the tone of the exhibition presented here.

Following an age-old tradition, our first reaction to gold is to consider its monetary value. In so doing, we fall into step with the Spanish conquerors. Wherever they landed, their first concern was gold. Political power and the conversion of pagan nations — the avowed goals of Cortez[4] and Pizarro as well as of the men who fought under them — were soon forgotten whenever there was mention of a treasure. Their appetite for precious metals was insatiable. Atahualpa sought in vain to satisfy it, first by offering, then by delivering, a huge ransom. The offer made by the Inca the day after his capture was reported as follows:

The next day, Pizarro was with Atahualpa and sought to console him by telling him that he would not be killed. The king, while complaining of his humiliation and chains, was already very aware of what the Spaniards coveted above everything else. To gain his freedom, he said that he was prepared to give the

The first encounter of Fransisco Pizarro, the Spanish conqueror of Peru, and Atahualpa, the last Inca Emperor.

Spaniards as many objects of gold and silver as were required to fill the room in which he was kept prisoner up to an imaginary line he drew by raising his arm, on condition that the vessels would not be crushed before the full ransom had been delivered.[5]

It is obvious that there was misunderstanding on both sides: Pizarro considered gold as a guarantee and token of wealth, while the Inca saw it as a material of practical use which could be let go with little difficulty or worry. What the king promised his enemy was, certainly, something precious in his own eyes, but not the very essence of economic and personal triumph that it was to the Spaniards. The confusion caused by these conflicting valuations of gold was to be of short duration. Gold quickly became the "common" metal Atahualpa had spoken of, but not in his sense of the term. It was now a symbol of riches for Indians and Spanish alike — the "filthy lucre" which was both base and highly desirable at the same time. To finish the story: the treasure delivered by Atahualpa was promptly inventoried, then crushed and melted into ingots. All that is left of it is a memory. In order to attempt to understand the role played by gold for the Incas and for the cultures that preceded them, let us view it under two aspects: *The Gold of the Living* and *The Gold of the Dead*.

The Gold of the Living

The chroniclers of the discovery and conquest of Peru speak of the many uses to which gold was put in the Inca society. It covered the walls of temples and decorated the thrones and litters of rulers and priests.[6] Statuettes and sculptures of gold were used in religious and sacrificial ceremonies. Ritual vases of every size were skilfully hammer-wrought from sheets of the yellow metal. Dignitaries wore clothing on which thin gold ornaments, plain or embossed, were sewn. Crowns, masks, sceptres, and jewellery were made of the same material.

The intrinsic beauty of gold fascinated the Indians to such an extent that they saw in it a reflection of the gods.[7] The Incas, being divine rulers, drew their authority from the sun and claimed to be its direct descendants. The brilliance of the sun, its warm colours ranging from red to white and including all the shades of orange and yellow, could best be symbolized by gold. The rays of the sun striking on temple and palace walls sheathed with gold would dazzle the eyes of spectators. The gold became, in a sense, an agent of the sun, transmitting its light, warmth, and life to the viewer.

Cuzco, the holy city and capital of the Incas, contained not only the chief centre of adoration, called *Coricancha* or "the palace of the sun", but also the palaces of the earthly rulers. This city, with its treasures, was seen by three Spaniards — Martin Bueno, Pedro Martin, and a man called Zarate.[8] Pizarro, in order to discover if Atahualpa had truly arranged for the amassing of the treasure, sent these men, on February 15, 1533, on a reconnaissance mission to the capital of the Incas, where they remained for nearly four months. "The buildings are covered with great sheets of gold on the side of the rising sun, while on the shady side the gold is less pure." Within the courtyard was a representation of the sun itself: ". . . a disc of gold twice as thick as those covering the walls . . . it was a round face surrounded by rays and flames." The travellers went on: "There was so much gold in the town that it was astonishing." Again, the only records of these splendours are written documents, since the gold itself was either ripped off and melted into ingots or destroyed by the Indians themselves in their despair at the calamity that had befallen them.

The Gold of the Dead

Anyone visiting the ruins of Peru today will search in vain for traces of what has just been described; yet the museums of Lima and other cities in Peru, as well as other museums throughout the world, display collections of ancient Peruvian objects in gold and other precious metals. These works of art were discovered long after the Spanish Conquest in huge pre-Columbian cemeteries scattered all over Peru. What we know of the prehistory of Peru, of its succession of civilizations and cultures, comes to a great extent from the study of objects buried in tombs. Our exhibition is made up of objects recovered from the ground, mostly from graves.

The cult of the dead, practised among the Incas and in the pre-Inca cultures, required that the deceased, especially if he had belonged to the ruling class, be mummified and placed in a burial chamber furnished with offerings. Some of the most exquisite textiles ever produced by man, as well as varied and splendid ceramics, beautifully ornamented tools in wood and metal, semi-precious stones, and objects in gold and other metals, accompanied the corpse. Mummies were wrapped in the superb fabrics we have just mentioned. Many were topped with an artificial head, carved in wood or shaped like a cushion, and covered with a gold mask in an effort to recreate a human appearance.[9] Gold objects were often inserted among the fabrics, sewn on to them or placed as the deceased would have worn them during his lifetime; for example, a necklace would encircle the throat.

17

For an aesthetic appreciation of the Gold of the Dead we must try to understand the cult to which it was devoted. It is quite obvious that gold, for the ancient Peruvians, was not a treasure in the Western sense of the word. Masks, diadems, necklaces, and the gold coverings fashioned for parts of the human body were intended to vanish forever. Buried in graves, they were not intended to be recovered. In short, they were eliminated from the economy; they were to belong *ad aeternam* to the deceased. Were they objects that he had accumulated during his lifetime with the express purpose of taking them into the after-world? Or were they chosen by his family after his death in observance of traditional rites? It is impossible to know for sure. However, the figurative ceramics of the Inca and pre-Inca cultures, make it clear that the personal adornments found in tombs are not different from those worn by the living. The ancient Peruvians were fond of earrings and ear-plugs; they pierced their nasal septum with rings; they wore necklaces and drank out of vessels like those they took with them to their graves. The Gold of the Dead, therefore, bears a close relationship to the Gold of the Living in purpose and style.

There are, however, some preserved objects whose original use is more puzzling and whose role in the world of the living is unclear. There are, for example, the thousands of gold plaques preserved in the Museo "Oro del Peru". Rectangular and circular in form, varying in size from less than an inch in diameter to almost twelve inches long, and reportedly found in tombs, their purpose remains obscure. At present they are used to decorate the walls and doorways of the Museum. Were they used thus in the past, to decorate walls in funerary chambers? Or were they simply offerings placed in the tomb after removal from the walls of a temple which they had originally ornamented? Did they, in fact, serve the same purpose as the plaques seen in Cuzco and described by Pizarro's emissaries? Nothing can be stated with certainty. These plaques were among the objects collected by Don Miguel in an effort to preserve the cultural patrimony of his country; their original context in the tombs — which, if recorded, might have given a clue to their use — has been lost.

There is one strange feature of the gold from these tombs which may be significant. Many of the objects were painted; some were even polychromed. Evidently there was sometimes a desire to alter or disguise the appearance of gold in ancient times. The brilliant reflection mentioned by the three Spaniards who saw the *Coricancha* at Cuzco was sometimes concealed. The viewer may verify this statement by examining the backrest from a royal litter (237) where numerous figures carved in wood all bear ornaments in gold showing traces of paint. Precious as it was, gold was often subordinated to painted decoration. Such treatment further indicates that gold did not have the absolute intrinsic value in the eyes of the ancient Peruvians that it has for us.

Such a judgment might be thought to be contradicted by the accounts given by the Spanish chroniclers[10] — no doubt derived from native informants — of the conquest of the Chimu Empire by the Incas about 1470. We are told that Tupac Inca Yupanqui, son and future successor to the throne of his father, Pachacutec Inca Yupanqui, captured Chan Chan, the Chimu capital, and sacked it. He seized a large quantity of gold and silver and ordered that the Chimu craftsmen be transferred to Cuzco. The golden loot was melted down and transformed into a number of large objects of veneration placed in the temple of *Coricancha*. Specifically, it is said that the representation of the sun, admired by the three Spaniards to whom we have referred above, was created from gold confiscated at Chan Chan.

One might see a cruel irony in these historical events: Pachacutec had the same appetites as Pizarro; the pillaging of Chan Chan had its counterpart in the dark episode of Cajamarca and in the sacking of Cuzco. We believe, however, that there was a fundamental difference between the attitude of the Inca and that of his Spanish conqueror. The former maintained the ritual character of gold by transforming it into objects of veneration; the other converted most of it into anonymous ingots. For the 16th-century Spaniard, gold was primarily a matter of personal riches, while for the Inca the ceremonial use of the noble metal remained foremost.

The tombs of ancient Peru have revealed a wealth of works of art, not only gold and silver objects but also high quality ceramics, textiles displaying the great skills of their weavers, and carvings in stone, wood, and other materials. The overwhelming attraction of the works in precious metals does not reside in the fact that they are made of gold or silver, but rather that their form and craftsmanship testify to the genius of artists whose names remain unknown and whose histories will never be told. This exhibition is — over and above its dedication to gold as a leitmotif — a testimony to the imagination and aesthetic achievements of the ancient Peruvian artists, who, in their work, speak the universal language of human creativity.

Notes

1. M. Jeronimo Benzoni, *La Historia del Mundo Nuevo* [Venice, 1565]. Translated into Spanish by Carlos Radicati di Primeglio (Lima: Universidad de San Marcos, 1967), p. 7.

2. Miguel Cabello de Balboa, *Miscelanea Antartica: una historia del Peru antiguo* [1586] (Lima: Universidad de San Marcos, 1951), p. 471. Balboa qualifies the word "stolen" in a parenthesis where he prudently remarks, "if it is permitted to use this term".

3. Benzoni, *op. cit.,* p. 11.

4. Hernando Cortéz, the Spanish conqueror, who in 1521 seized Tenochtitlan, the Aztec capital, today Mexico City.

5. Benzoni, *op. cit.,* p. 9.

6. Speaking of the city of Carangue in southern Ecuador, the birth-place of Atahualpa, Cieza de Léon says: "The walls of the temples were covered with plates of gold and silver." See Cieza de Léon, *La Cronica del Peru* [Seville, 1553] (Madrid: Espasa-Calpe, S.A., 1962), p. 123.

7. It is reported that the Incas described gold as "the sweat of the sun" and silver as "the tears of the moon"; see André Emmerich, *Sweat of the Sun and Tears of the Moon* (Seattle: University of Washington Press, 1965) p. xix. For the Aztecs of Mexico, the term "teocuitlatl", used to designate gold in the *nahuatl* language, means "the excrement of the gods"; *ibid.*

8. The account of their visit and the translation of the texts relative to it are given in John Hemming, *The Conquest of the Inca* (New York; Toronto: Macmillan, 1970) pp. 63 ff.

9. The large mummy displayed in the Museo de Arte in Lima has an artificial head wearing a golden mask. It dates from the Huari/Tiahuanaco period.

10. Cabello de Balboa, *op. cit.,* pp. 332 ff.

Peru: the Land and Its People
Kent C. Day

Geography and Natural Resources

Peru is situated on the Pacific coast of South America approximately 7,000 kilometres (4,000 miles) south of Toronto and Montreal and somewhat south-by-east of Winnipeg. The entire country lies within the Tropic of Capricorn, and its far northern frontier nearly touches the Equator. Clockwise from the north, Peru is bordered by Ecuador, Colombia, Brazil, Bolivia, and Chile.

The Pacific shore of Peru is a narrow strip of desert interrupted by some fifty river valleys more or less equally spaced along the coast. Although several of the valleys are dry all the year round, others have perennial or seasonal streams fed by rainfall in the nearby highlands. Barren foothills of the Andes parallel the coastal desert. Within 100 kilometres of the coast, the foothills merge with the western range of the Andes. A high plateau, lakes, and a few deep intermontane valleys divide this range from the peaks of the eastern range of the Andes. The eastern range receives a greater amount of precipitation than the plateau or western range, and most of its drainage flows north and east into tributaries of the Amazon River. The heavy rainfall, dense jungle, and tropical lowlands characteristic of the eastern face of the Andes and the Amazon Basin contrast dramatically with the nearby snow-capped mountain peaks, the high, cold plateaus and arid slopes of the western range, and the desert coast. Within these major topographic and environmental zones, there are myriad subtle changes caused by differences in elevation, soils, drainage patterns, and rainfall. In broad terms, however, the western coastal valleys, high intermontane valleys and plateaus, eastern mountain slopes, and tropical lowlands are distinct resource areas that have been exploited by man for thousands of years.

In Peru, vegetation and animal life are varied and quite different from the plants and animals of North America. A large number of plants and a few animals native to Peru were cultivated and domesticated long before Europeans came to South America. Many varieties of potatoes and a grain called *quinoa* were first domesticated in the Peruvian highlands. *Coca* shrubs were planted and tended prehistorically on the eastern and western flanks of the Andes. Both brown and white cotton were cultivated extensively in the coastal valleys, along with corn, beans, chilis, avocados, and peanuts, and probably tobacco, tomatoes, and sweet potatoes. *Yuca, lucuma, chirimoya, oca,* and *caigua* are the common local names for some of the distinctive Peruvian fruits and vegetables not usually found beyond the tropics.

Llamas, alpacas, and guinea pigs were domesticated in Peru and used for their wool or meat. Llamas were also used to transport light loads. Vicuña were probably not domesticated, but herds were maintained and their delicate wool reserved for making fine cloth for Inca royalty.[1]

Deer, monkeys, sea lions, large cats, foxes, parrots, cormorants, pelicans, snakes, lizards, fish, insects, and other creatures native to Peru were depicted on prehistoric ceramics.

Many semi-precious stones were used by the ancient Peruvians in jewellery and as inlays in metalwork, carved wooden boxes, incised and carved stone, shell and bone plaques, and ornaments of various kinds. Amethysts and rock crystal are found in the central Peruvian highlands but are more common in Bolivia, Brazil, and Argentina. Turquoise occurs in Peru but can easily be confused with the more common chrysocolla. As no tests of the stone were possible before this catalogue was produced, we have used the term "turquoise" loosely to cover both stones. Lapis lazuli is found in Chile. Other stones that have been identified are quartz crystals of various kinds, geodes, and pyrites. Gem-quality stones, however, are very rare in Peru; the emeralds used to adorn the eyes of funerary masks, for instance, were probably brought to Peru from Ecuador or Colombia.[2]

Peru has extensive and rich deposits of metallic ores. Copper, silver, gold, and some tin were surface-mined by the Inca, and copper, silver, and gold were mined even earlier. These metals were smelted and worked with simple tools and were fashioned into objects that ranged from the common pin to surgical instruments, crowns, masks, and wide bands fixed to buildings.

Exploitation of marine resources has played a major role in the economy of Peru since prehistoric times. The continental shelf off the west coast of Peru is narrow and plunges into the Peru–Chile trench within a few kilometres of the shoreline. Cold water wells upward along the face of the trench, bringing with it a constant supply of dissolved minerals and organic material that is consumed by plankton. The plankton forms the base of a life chain of fishes, birds, sea mammals, and shellfish that is one of the richest in the world. The cold water, known as the Humboldt Current, eventually flows northward along the Peruvian coast toward the Equator. On occasion this current is overwhelmed by a surge of warm water from the north, and the change in temperature temporarily disrupts normal conditions. The nutrient content of the water is drastically reduced, and sea life either perishes or moves to colder water farther from shore or deeper in the sea. Once the upwelling resumes, the usual abundance of sea life quickly returns.

The cold water that supports the marine life affects the climate along the coast and, in a sense, creates the coastal desert. Each day, as the land is heated by radiant energy from the sun, the air above it is warmed and rises, evaporating moisture as it does so. As it rises, cool, supersaturated air from the sea is drawn inland. Depending on the season of the year, the sea air covers the coast with fog or, as it is heated by the land, expands and absorbs even more moisture. In either event, the incoming sea air hardly ever condenses to the point where precipitation occurs. As a result, the vegetation along the coast is limited to xerophytic plants collectively called *lomas* that flourish seasonally from moisture supplied by fog. In the coastal valleys, the natural vegetation depends upon ground water or river water. When water is diverted from streams into irrigation channels, the alluvial soils in the valleys and the warm temperate climate combine to make the valleys prime agricultural land. Although not as extensive as ancient irrigation systems, modern irrigation in the coastal valleys supports extensive crops of sugar cane, rice, cotton, corn, alfalfa, fruits, vegetables, and some vineyards. These crops are not sufficient, however, to feed the present population of the country. Even the immense resources of the sea are in danger of depletion from over-fishing and the production of fishmeal, most of which is exported for cattle feed, chicken feed, and pet food.

Peru Before the Spanish Conquest

Most people have a passing acquaintance with the Inca and identify them as the prehistoric inhabitants of Peru. The oldest archaeological remains attributed to the Inca, however, are no earlier than about A.D. 1200[3], and the famous Inca empire was in existence for less than a century before the arrival of the Spanish in 1532. Normally, a tourist in Peru visits the former Inca capital of Cuzco and makes a side trip to Machu Picchu, one of the few excavated Inca sites. In Lima, however, the visitor has the opportunity to see large collections of artifacts, textiles, and ceramics made by some of the other ancient inhabitants of Peru, particularly those who lived on the coast.

Although the present exhibition is generally limited to gold and silver objects which were probably made between about 200 B.C. and A.D. 1500, the purpose of this brief essay is to present an outline of the nearly ten-thousand-year period of human occupation in Peru

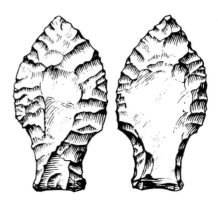

Obverse and reverse sides of a fluted fish-tail projectile point typical of those used by early hunters in Peru, Ecuador, and Chile. From Gordon R. Willey: An Introduction to American Archaeology, Volume Two, South America © *1971 by Prentice-Hall, Inc. Reproduced by permission of Prentice-Hall. Inc.*

that preceded the manufacture of these objects. Our evidence for this cultural history is almost entirely archaeological, although there is also some ethnohistoric material available for the time period when the metal objects were made. Since most of the objects in this exhibition are from the Peruvian coast, particularly the north coast, the archaeology of that area is emphasized. It should be pointed out, however, that the ancient cultures of the north coast did not develop in isolation. For one thing, much of the metal used in ancient Peru probably came from the highlands. In addition, there was probably contact between the coast and the highlands throughout much of Peruvian prehistory.

Peruvian gold and silver — probably made into objects similar to those on view here — played a major role in the Spanish conquest of Peru. In a broad sense Peruvian archaeology began during the Spanish Colonial period, when the conquerors looted Inca temples and palaces and zealous priests searched out pagan sanctuaries and burials in order to destroy them and eradicate idolatry. During this process it soon became evident that ancient burials frequently contained gold and silver offerings, and organized mining of prehistoric sites became a profitable enterprise. Looting has continued uninterrupted ever since, as museums and private collec-

tors throughout the world have eagerly sought the objects excavated by talented robbers.

During the 19th century expeditions came to Peru from abroad to collect materials for museums and universities. It was during this time that formal archaeology was initiated and some controlled excavations conducted. By the early 20th century the general outline of most of Peruvian history was known, even though some of the dates assigned to the cultural stages were inexact. Since that time a great deal of effort has gone into refining the chronological sequence of ancient Peruvian cultures. In addition, work on the earliest periods of human occupation in Peru has received increased attention in recent years. At present, research programmes organized by Peruvian, Canadian, United States, European, and Japanese institutions are active in the field.

Early Hunters

Descendants of the first settlers of the New World reached Tierra del Fuego, the southern tip of South America, by about 9000 to 7000 B.C. These people made a distinctive obsidian projectile point with a fish-tail-shaped base. These early inhabitants lived in caves and apparently dined on an extinct form of ground sloth and, perhaps, horse. Similar stone points have also been

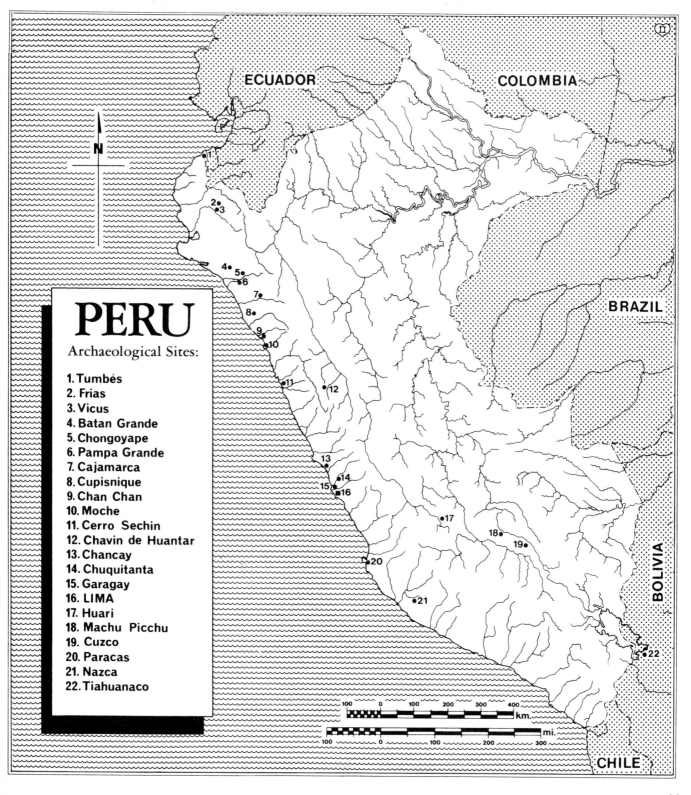

PERU

Archaeological Sites:

1. Tumbés
2. Frias
3. Vicus
4. Batan Grande
5. Chongoyape
6. Pampa Grande
7. Cajamarca
8. Cupisnique
9. Chan Chan
10. Moche
11. Cerro Sechin
12. Chavin de Huantar
13. Chancay
14. Chuquitanta
15. Garagay
16. LIMA
17. Huari
18. Machu Picchu
19. Cuzco
20. Paracas
21. Nazca
22. Tiahuanaco

ECUADOR

COLOMBIA

BRAZIL

BOLIVIA

CHILE

found in Peru and Ecuador, in caves and at open sites, and it is likely that their makers lived off the land by hunting.[4]

Chipped stone objects have been reported from Venezuela, Peru, Bolivia, and Argentina, some of which may be older than the obsidian fish-tail points. Stratified deposits in a group of caves and rock shelters in the south-central Peruvian highlands contain stone objects in the deepest strata which are about 19,000 years old. It is questionable, however, whether these ancient objects were shaped by man. On the other hand, the stone materials from slightly higher deposits in the same caves were undoubtedly worked by human hands. These tools, together with other stone tools from stratified caves in the highlands and on the southern coast of Peru, antedate the fish-tail points and indicate that man was living in the Andean area by at least 10,000 B.C.[5]

Some of the other early inhabitants on the Peruvian coast made long stone points with small parallel-sided stems or bases. Like other early hunters, these people lived near rock shelters or used open localities for their sites. They also had chipping stations near outcrops of fine-grained stone. At the time when these tools were made — probably about 10,000 to 6000 B.C. — the coastal valleys were probably more heavily wooded than at present, and game was abundant. As witness to this, piles of mastodon bones occur in what are now some of the most desolate areas along the coast, between river valleys or in dry tributaries of the valleys. On occasion, large quantities of stone tools have been found in the vicinity of the bones, but it has been difficult to prove that the people who made the easily recognizable long points slaughtered the mastodons. Radiocarbon dates on the bones of the extinct elephants show that the animals were alive when the long points were being made. There is also evidence that an extinct form of horse, giant armadillo, and *carabaya* were contemporary with the mastodons and the men who made the long points. For lack of any other information about the way of life of the people who made the points, it is assumed that they hunted the large animals or scavenged their carcasses.[6]

A hunting and gathering economy persisted in the highlands and on the coast of Peru for a few thousand years after the disappearance of the large game animals. During this time, chipped stone implements changed and grinding stones were added to the inventory of campsite tools. It is believed, therefore, that small game — essentially the animals that still inhabit the coast and highlands — were hunted and that plants, seeds, and fruits were gathered.[7]

Early Settlers

Between 3500 and 2500 B.C. there were campsites on coastal hillsides, where *lomas* plants flourish seasonally. Chipped stone points and grinding implements found at these sites are evidence that the inhabitants lived in the *lomas* fields to exploit the edible tubers, bulbs, and rhizomes produced by these plants. The settlers probably also hunted the grazing animals drawn to the verdant hillsides during the months when the *lomas* were succulent. It is possible that some of the campers came from the highlands in pursuit of migrating game, but it is more likely that most of the hunters and gatherers came to the *lomas* from nearby valleys.[8] The time of year when the *lomas* grow is also the time when coastal rivers are at their lowest. Perhaps both the game and the people were attracted to the *lomas* because the valleys were undergoing an annual "winter" dry season and forage was scarce. This would be difficult to prove, however, because extensive and intensive later occupation of the valleys has destroyed most evidence of any seasonal "summer" campsites when water, plants, and animals were probably more abundant in the valleys.

By about 2500 B.C., the *lomas* camps had been abandoned and permanent settlements were made on the coastline. For some unexplained reason, the early coastal peoples suddenly began to exploit marine resources intensively. The sites inhabited by these people were not randomly chosen but were carefully located to take advantage of certain resources. For instance, sites near rocky sections of the shore have deep deposits of remains of shellfish that live among rocks. Other sites located a few hundred metres away, but near sandy or muddy shores, have remains of shellfish which burrow into the bottom. Since there are few interruptions in the stratified deposits of these sites, it is evident that occupation was continuous and that the residents relied almost entirely on the marine creatures close at hand. Curiously, there is little evidence that shellfish gathered from one kind of habitat were exchanged for shellfish gathered from another, even when the settlements were close neighbours.[9]

Preservation of organic material is excellent at many of the shoreline sites occupied between 2500 and 1700 B.C. Cotton textiles and gourds have been found at several of these amid the deep deposits of organic debris.[10] These two plants were the first to be cultivated on the Peruvian coast. Because neither plant grows near the shoreline or is part of the *lomas* vegetation, it is apparent that both were cultivated in the river valleys and the fibres and fruits brought to the shoreline sites. From the large quantity of cotton textiles recovered from these sites, it is evident that a large acreage somewhere in the valleys was devoted to the cultivation of cotton.[11] Unlike modern hybrids, native Peruvian cotton produces only one harvest a year. This long growing season is another indication that cotton was cultivated on a large scale; there would not have been a sufficient harvest from casual gathering to supply the heavy demand evidenced by the quantity of textiles found by the archaeologist.

Cultivation of two inedible plants long before the invention or introduction of ceramics, and before widespread cultivation of the standard New World vegetable staples, corn, beans, and squash, was one of the major accomplishments of the ancient inhabitants of Peru. Because of the lack of rainfall, it has always been necessary to irrigate crops in the coastal valleys of Peru. Perhaps the early cotton farmers used flood-water irrigation, but even this method, if used continuously for a year, would have necessitated the construction of some sort of headgates and ditches. The running water itself probably made ditches among the plants as they were irrigated time after time before the harvest. Possibly this natural effect of running water was recognized and

improved upon by these early people. Unfortunately, there are no traces of fields and ditches in the valleys as old as the shoreline sites.

Many of the early coastal settlements were maintained over a long period of time. A few of the larger sites have complex groups of platforms, plazas, and sunken circular courts. Some of these structures were built of split stone or cobbles gathered from nearby seacliffs, hills, or gravel beds. The size and complexity of these sites indicate that there was a fairly large population nearby which was called upon to furnish the labour to construct the more elaborate buildings.[12]

Near the end of this time period, sites were built in the lower parts of the valleys, some of which contain large masonry structures. The site of Chuquitanta, near Lima, has a large rectangular structure divided into several chambers and corridors. This building is located at one end of two long, parallel rows of unexcavated structures that may have been residences.[13] Although the large building at Chuquitanta has been referred to as a ceremonial structure, it may have served the more mundane purpose of a central storehouse for cotton or textiles. In any case, there is evidence at this site for the manufacture of twined textiles and the first use of the heddle loom.

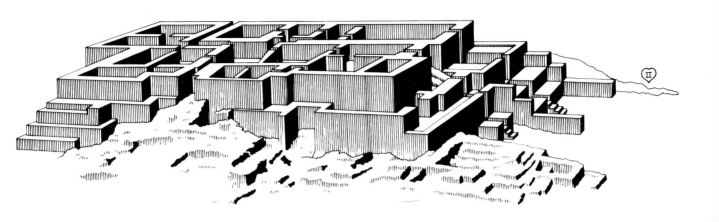

The extensive cultivation of cotton, the manufacture of cotton textiles, the construction of elaborate buildings, and perhaps the initial use of irrigation on the Peruvian coast are evidence that these coastal people, who drew most of their subsistence from the sea, were numerous and well organized. Their accomplishments were such that subsequent Peruvian prehistory can be viewed as a series of variations on the themes of centralized control of economic resources, emphasis upon textiles as a vital manufactured product, and use of organized labour in the construction of public buildings.

Some archaeologists believe that ceramic technology was introduced to the New World by means of accidental trans-Pacific contact from Neolithic Japan to the west coast of South America about 2500 B.C. This hypothesis is supported by a striking similarity of clay figurines and decorated vessels found in southern Japan with those found at Valdivia on the Ecuadorian coast.[14] However, ceramics have been found in Colombia and in new excavations at the site of Valdivia which antedate these.[15] Although the similarities between the Japanese and Ecuadorian ceramics possibly represent long-distance contact, it is quite clear that ceramic technology had already developed in South America before such contact occurred.

Despite this reservation about the significance of long-distance contact, it is likely that pottery was introduced to Peru from elsewhere, perhaps from the north (Colombia and Ecuador) via the intermontane valleys in the Peruvian highlands. Although some very crude ceramics have been found on the northern coast of Peru, these vessels are not well documented and could be poor-quality copies of other, better-made ceramics. Therefore it is also possible that ceramic technology first developed on the eastern foothills of the Andes, spreading into the highlands and from there to the coast.[16] Unless some new discoveries of very early pottery are made in Peru, the evidence now points to some outside source in the north or east.

Just before pottery was introduced to Peru, corn (maize) began to be cultivated. The archaeological record of the south-central highlands shows that corn was probably domesticated there before it was cultivated on the coast. This early highland corn was apparently native to South America and not one of the varieties believed to have been introduced from Mexico. The early corn from the coast was a primitive Peruvian variety, *Confite Morocho*.[17] Although the potato was probably cultivated in the highlands at this time, no archaeological evidence of its use has yet been found.

Carved human figure on a slab at Cerro Sechin.

Some of the large shoreline sites continued to be occupied during this period, but with the increased emphasis on agriculture more and more settlements were built in the coastal valleys. Large ceremonial sites were also built in the highlands, particularly in areas where agriculture was feasible.

Cult Centres and the Origin of Theocratic Kingdoms: Chavin, Cupisnique, Sechin, Paracas

After about 1800 B.C., such developments as those just described — the broadening of the agricultural base and the domestication of the llama, the achievement of proficiency in weaving and other crafts such as pottery, the growing efficiency in the management of communal affairs in villages and towns through religious and civic controls, as evidenced by the construction of major ceremonial and public buildings — ceased to belong to scattered communities and were disseminated throughout the country. The number of archaeological sites increases, an indication of a rapidly growing population. It was against this background that a widespread art style developed in Peru, which takes its name — Chavin — from the site of Chavin de Huantar in the east-central highlands. This site, which was occupied between 800 and 200 B.C., has an imposing group of masonry build-

ings, some of which have carved lintels and doorjambs. One of the major buildings has underground galleries. An anthropomorphic carved stone pillar called the *lanzon* is located in the intersection of two of these galleries. The *lanzon* and other carved stones depict birds, serpents, and snarling cats.[18] Frequently these elements, particularly the snakes and cats, were combined, or some of their characteristics added to anthropomorphic figures. The style in which these figures were carved is distinctive and easily recognizable. It was repeated on ceramics, goldwork, and textiles. Carved stone heads, slightly larger than lifesize, were tenoned to some of the buildings at Chavin de Huantar. Similar tenon heads have been found elsewhere in the highlands, as have other carved stone monuments which probably were parts of buildings.

On the north coast a similar style, with felines, serpents, and fanged human faces, is known as Cupisnique. Ceramics, goldwork, and a few specimens of carved shell have been found decorated in this style. At Cerro Sechin on the central coast there is a rectangular structure with curved corners which is almost completely faced with carved stone slabs. The designs on these slabs, possibly re-used in this building, are primarily human figures or parts of human bodies that appear to have been dis-

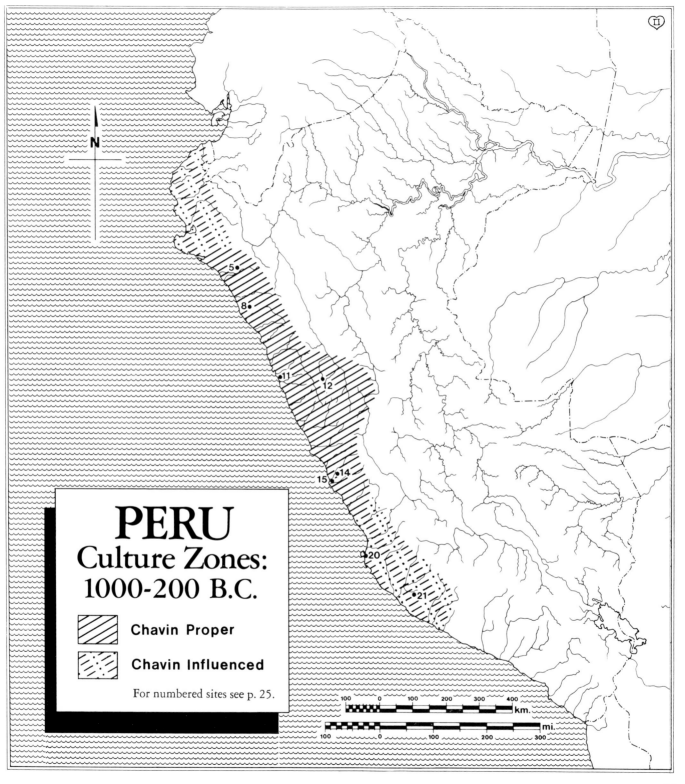

PERU
Culture Zones:
1000-200 B.C.

Chavin Proper

Chavin Influenced

For numbered sites see p. 25.

Relief sculpture from Chavin de Huantar of a feline being with serpent attributes. Length, 1 m. From Gordon R. Willey: An Introduction to American Archaeology, Volume Two, South America © *1971 by Prentice-Hall, Inc. Reproduced by permission of Prentice-Hall, Inc.*

membered. Buried beneath this building is another rectangular structure built of adobe. Remains of creatures with large claws appear at each side of an entrance to a staircase in the façade of this buried building. They are painted in black, red, and white over a coating of clay plaster. Incised and painted figures of fish also appear on this structure.[19] At other sites along the central and north coast stylized feline heads, massive serpent heads, and other figures have been found sculpted and incised on the clay-covered adobe façades of buildings. Several years ago part of an incised and painted column was found on the north coast, but it has since been destroyed.[20]

Within the last year excavations have been conducted at the site of Garagay, near Lima. One of the stone structures at this site has a series of large modelled and painted clay figures with fanged heads on its façade.[21] Pottery with incised designs similar to the stone sculpture and incised figures on adobe buildings has been found in the far north and on the south coast of Peru. The early pottery and textiles of Paracas, for instance, adopted Chavin motifs but adapted them to local techniques and traditions.

Although the roots of this art style are probably quite ancient, the particular iconographic configuration of

carved and incised felines, serpents, birds, and human figures known as Chavin, Cupisnique, Sechin, or Paracas is the first widespread art style in Peru. Whether this style originated in the highlands or on the coast, its rapid dissemination could represent the work of missionaries who propagated a powerful religious cult symbolized, like Christianity, by semi-realistic designs.[22] Since hardly anything is known about the economic activities and social organization of the people who spread the art style, it is difficult to say anything definite about the culture that sustained the art style and cult. It is assumed, however, that agriculture was the common subsistence base, that corn was cultivated, and that llamas and alpacas were fully domesticated and raised in large numbers for their wool and meat and for use as beasts of burden. In the search for the origins of the Chavin and related art styles, it is often overlooked that the general unity of the style could indicate economic and political unification of the coast and the highlands. The range of variation within the style, on the other hand, could indicate the existence of regional centres where not only ceremonial activities but economic and social transactions took place. In other words, this first great art style may be one symptom of the fundamental cultural unity of Peru — a unity within a diversity resulting from climate, resources, and degree of

Painted mud-sculpture figure from Garagay near Lima. Note the stylistic similarity to the feline figure from Chavin de Huantar.

exploitation by man — which was briefly manifested through some form of centralized control.

Among the technological achievements of this period was metallurgy. Copper ornaments were made from smelted, hammered sheets of the metal. These objects have been found in Bolivia and on the south coast of Peru, an indication that copper-working originated in the south in the area where most of the copper deposits occur. Gold plaques, ear spools, crowns, nose ornaments, and pectorals all bear designs of the Chavin or its allied styles. Like copper, the gold objects were hammered from sheets and were ornamented in *repoussé* by beating. Certainly, by the end of the period the technique of *mise en couleur* for producing gold and silver finishes on alloys and the methods of joining several worked pieces together by welding or soldering had been perfected.

Up to this time most textiles had been made by twining. The heddle loom, probably used with a backstrap and anchored to a post or tree, now came into widespread use and, as a result, more complicated textiles were produced. Tapestry, pattern weaves, and gauze weaves were prepared, and some textiles were painted or embroidered with Chavin designs.

Coastal Kingdoms: Nazca, and Mochica to Chimu

The apparent unity achieved when the Chavin style was predominant was relatively short-lived. Despite the fact that certain vessel shapes and design motifs continued to be used, distinctive regional styles — some of them limited to a single valley — developed along the coast. In addition, the major Chavin centres in the highlands and on the coast were abandoned. Subsequently, other large sites were established, but even these were not occupied for long periods of time. Truncated pyramids, built of adobe or fieldstone-filled, and flanked by platforms and plazas, were constructed. Extensive sites consisting of what were probably residential quarters were built on hillsides overlooking cultivated valleys. This settlement pattern of dispersed rural communities and centralized ceremonial centres seems to have been typical throughout Peru at this period. Unfortunately, little excavation has been conducted around the perimeters of the ceremonial centres to determine whether or not they had resident populations.

Furthermore, with a few exceptions, most of the artifacts — primarily ceramics — are from looted cemeteries and therefore have limited value for the interpretation of their makers' social and economic organization. From such a cemetery, near a hill called Cerro

33

Vicus in the Upper Piura valley, and from a site called Frias further to the northeast — both in the extreme north of the country near the border with Ecuador — comes a large part of the early gold and silver in the Museo "Oro del Peru" collection, many pieces of which are included in the present exhibition. The pottery of Vicus betrays Chavinoid influences, while the Frias gold resembles in many respects the Vicus metal objects. On such stylistic grounds alone, the material from these two sites is ascribed to the last centuries of the first millennium B.C. and the beginning of the Christian era. Within the same time range, apparently, falls the fine gold jaguar found at Pampa Grande in the Lambayeque valley (19). As the range of Vicus pottery has led scholars to assign it a period of several centuries, and the style is related to that of the Mochica culture further south, it is possible to predicate several local variants of the Mochica culture; it is also conceivable that the Vicus style was antecedent to the Mochica ceramic development. In this catalogue, the material recorded as coming from Vicus is so noted, and may be considered as forming a transition between the Chavin tradition and the Mochica culture.

Apparently somewhat later than Vicus, or overlapping its later stages, is the culture represented by the gold from the Frias tombs. It too must be considered as "proto-Mochica" or early Mochica. While it is still impossible to say anything about the social organization, the economic life, and the architectural forms developed by the people who produced the Frias gold, the gold objects themselves provide important evidence for the state of the metallurgist's craft at this period (e.g., 83–88). As we shall see, the art of casting gold by the *cire perdue* method seems to have been known to them.

Possibly contemporary with Frias, but identified with the type-site of Salinar further to the south, is the culture which produced the two bone plaques in the exhibition (20, 21) described as "Chavinoid".

While there are still many uncertainties about the cultural stages which succeeded the Chavin, it is clear that about the time of Christ two major ceramic traditions emerged from the preceding regional diversity. On the north coast the dominant style is designated Mochica because it appears to have had its centre in the Moche valley. The Nazca style, named after the Nazca valley, is typical of the south coast.

Nazca

Some of the finest ceramics and textiles ever made in

34

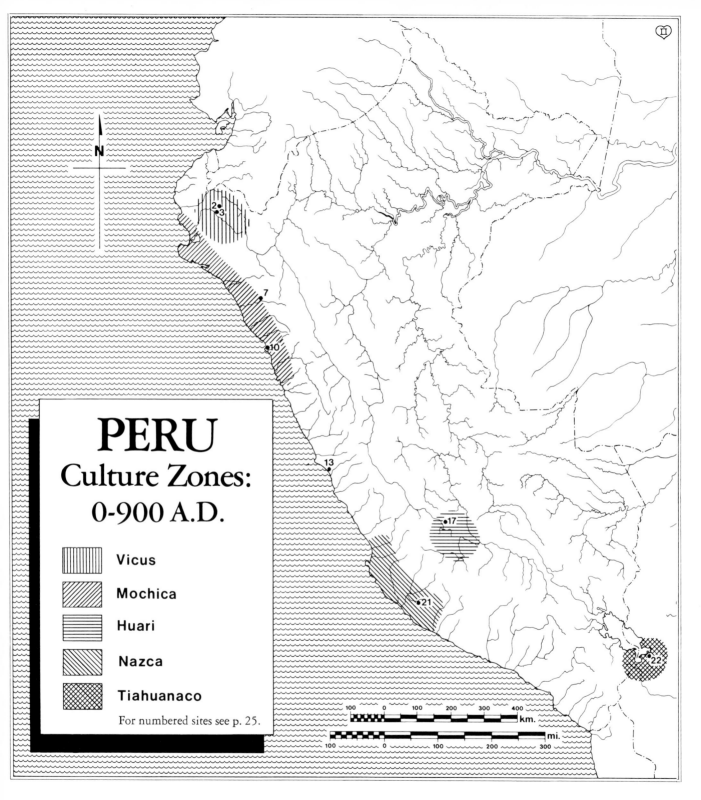

PERU
Culture Zones:
0-900 A.D.

Vicus

Mochica

Huari

Nazca

Tiahuanaco

For numbered sites see p. 25.

Aerial view of a few of the lines and a flower-like figure on the plateau near Nazca.

Peru were manufactured by the Nazca on the south coast. Complicated figures of animals, plants, and people were painted in polychrome colours on well-fired, highly burnished vessels. Some of the textiles contemporary with the pottery, especially those from the "Paracas Necropolis", are the wonder of modern weavers because of the fineness of the threads, the complexity of the designs, the permanence of the colours, and the elaborateness of the weaves and needlework. One of the characteristics of human figures depicted on the Nazca vessels and in textiles is a metal nose ornament or "mouth mask" (see 123, 124); the quality of Nazca featherwork and textiles is also illustrated (127 ff.). Another accomplishment of the Nazca people was the creation of huge lines and figures on the surface of coastal plateaus. Although the purpose of these earthworks is not clearly understood, some students believe the lines were used as sighting lines for astronomical observations.[23] Not all archaeologists would commit themselves to this interpretation, but none would agree that the lines were landing strips for omnipotent voyagers from outer space!

The Nazca civilization was submerged in about the 7th century by the political and cultural expansion of a state centred at Huari, in the southern highlands of Peru. There is no material in the exhibition representing this culture.

Mochica

While the Nazca people were thriving on the south coast and developing their distinctive ceramic and textile arts, the Mochica began construction of what became the largest adobe building in South America at the site of Moche, in the Moche valley on the north coast of Peru. This structure, called the Huaca del Sol, was a truncated, terraced pyramid about 300 metres long, 150 metres wide, and 50 metres high. Because of massive spoliation, it is difficult to reconstruct its original plan. It was probably an irregularly shaped rectangle with several different levels on its summit, like most other large Mochica pyramids, but it has also been suggested that the structure was cross-shaped in plan.[24] Nearby, an adobe building called the Huaca de la Luna is a multilevel platform built against the side of a hill. Although these two structures were built, added to, and remodelled, there is no indication that the building phases of the two buildings coincided with one another or occurred at regular intervals.

Large, truncated, multilevel adobe pyramids were

built in most of the north coast valleys between about A.D. 200 and 800. Even though most of these prominent structures have not been studied in detail, they usually share two features that indicate how labour was organized. The adobes in the structures frequently have simple, inscribed punched marks on one face, which have been interpreted as makers' marks to identify the individuals or groups who manufactured the adobes. Another characteristic of the truncated pyramids is that they were built in column-like sections, one section juxtaposed against or resting upon another section. The vertical joints between the sections interrupt the bonding of adobes (which is not always uniform even within a section) and add nothing to the structural stability of the building. At the Huaca del Sol there is a high correlation between certain makers' marks and particular sections of the structure. It has been suggested that the sections each represent the work of a task force, perhaps drawn from the same group that made the adobes, which was obliged to furnish a certain amount of labour for the construction of public buildings.[25]

The Mochica also painted polychrome, incised murals on the walls of these pyramids, and there is some evidence that entire structures were painted red or yellow or white. Figures depicted in the murals include frontal views of elaborately dressed men holding staffs, profile drawings of warriors and prisoners, and other persons who were probably religious or political leaders of some note.[26]

A limited amount of excavation was conducted recently in the area between the Huaca del Sol and the Huaca de la Luna. Before this work was done, it was presumed that the site consisted only of the two large, truncated pyramids surrounded by a large cemetery. Because of the massiveness of the two *huacas* and the fact that graves in the adjacent cemetery had been looted for nearly a century, it was thought that this site was the capital and major ceremonial centre of the Mochica. The new excavations do not alter this interpretation, but do demonstrate that there was a considerable amount of architecture at the site in addition to the two large *huacas*. Other large Mochica sites in other valleys probably also had complex architecture around the prominent pyramids and may not have been as "vacant" as formerly thought. In any event, the site of Moche was occupied continuously for several hundred years and at its zenith was probably the capital of a kingdom that reached along most of the north coast. Apparently the large Mochica sites in the other valleys were subsidiary capitals or administrative centres.

There are few examples of Mochica textiles, but those extant are as elaborate as the textiles made by the contemporary Nazca people to the south, although they differ in style. Cotton was the most common material used in Mochica weaving. Alpaca wool was also used, but nearly always in conjunction with cotton thread. Tapestry and warp-face fabrics were produced, but plain weave textiles were by far the most common.

In ceramics the Mochica produced a large number of vessels depicting human heads, human figures, animals, fruits, and vegetables in full round. The human representations are so individualized that they probably depict once-living persons. Besides the "portrait vessels", there are representations of diseased and disfigured people and graphic scenes of punishment, death, and birth. A popular theme of the ceramicists was sex in about as many combinations, positions, and dimensions as the human body can accommodate, as well as organs beyond proportions allowed to man.

A subsequent ceramic style within the Mochica sequence had fine line drawings in red paint over a cream background. Frequent depictions of armed men and warriors with captives lend credibility to the idea that the Mochica extended their imperial holdings through military conquest. Other scenes with captives take place before a pyramid that has a seated figure in a small building on its summit. On other vessels there are runners carrying bags, warriors brandishing weapons, birds, insects, animals, and plants. Some have scenes of deer being snared or chased by dogs and men. Sea craft built of reeds, bearing elaborately garbed men and surrounded by sea creatures, are another common design. Animated jars, bowls, and plates with tiny feet are shown pouring liquid from themselves or bearing food at a banquet scene. In sum, this particular style of Mochica pottery constitutes the most complete record we have of the activities of a prehistoric, non-literate Peruvian culture. Before the end of the Mochica period, however, the ceramics were often decorated in abstract and simple geometric designs instead of the earlier graphic representations, and unpainted black pottery came into widespread use.

The love of natural forms and the ability to depict them vividly are also very evident in Mochica metalwork, even though the present exhibition does not contain many examples. The ear ornaments (104, 105, 106, 117, 118), however, typify the skill of the craftsman; although the masks (114, 115) do not have a firm provenance, their sensitivity suggests strongly that they belong to this period. It is also possible that some of the

Two representations of litters from line drawings on Mochica pots.
After Rafael Larco Hoyle, Los Mochicas *(Lima: Casa editoria
"La Cronica" y "Variedades", 1938); a Chancay litter is depicted
in the funerary group of no. 250.*

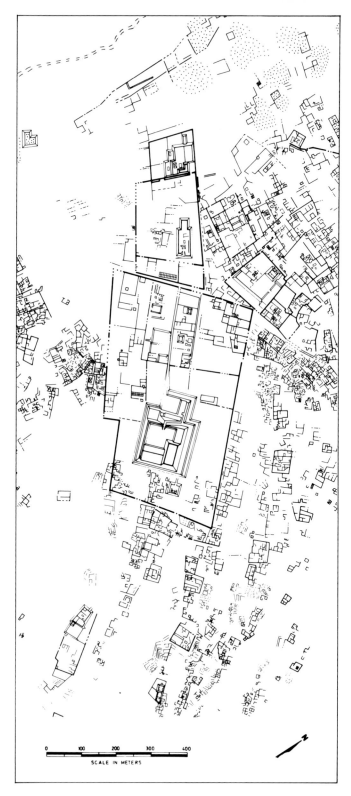

0   100   200   300   400
SCALE IN METERS

Central part of Pampa Grande, a late
Mochica site on the north coast of Peru.

masks and other objects which depict faces with an upswept outer corner of the eyelid (e.g., 143, 145, 179, 180, 226, etc.) are variants of Mochica art produced in the Lambayeque valley, north of the Moche valley — perhaps, in many cases, from a single site named Batan Grande. On the other hand, they may be later than the Mochica period; some of them are embossed with designs more typical of the Chimu, a people who occupied most of the north coast from about A.D. 1200 to 1470. The mixture of motifs and designs suggests, in fact, that these objects are transitional, but it is more prudent to assign them to the Chimu period, as we do here, until further research provides a definite answer.

Some time between about A.D. 600 and 800, the Mochica capital in the Moche valley was abandoned and a large site was established in the Lambayeque valley, 250 kilometres to the north. Although the Mochica continued to occupy valleys to the south of Lambayeque, Pampa Grande, built at a formerly unoccupied site, soon became the largest Mochica settlement on the north coast of Peru. Like the site of Moche, Pampa Grande is dominated by two large, truncated pyramids, the larger nearly the same size as the Huaca del Sol. The two *huacas* at Pampa Grande are surrounded by large adobe-walled, rectangular enclosures and at least twenty other

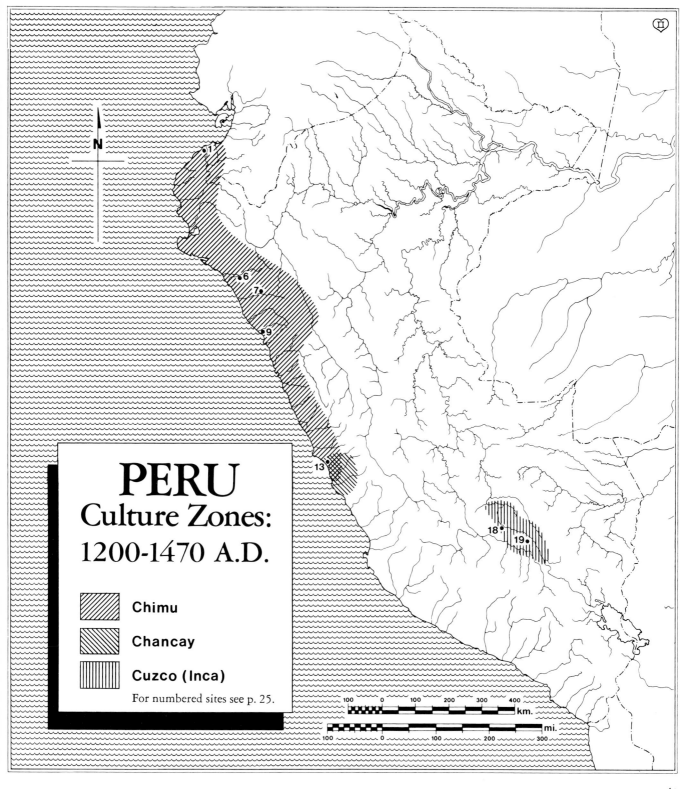

PERU
Culture Zones:
1200-1470 A.D.

Chimu

Chancay

Cuzco (Inca)

For numbered sites see p. 25.

N

100 0 100 200 300 400
km.

100 0 100 200 300
mi.

smaller *huacas* are scattered throughout the site area. There are also rectangular enclosures of various sizes, zones of compactly arranged stone masonry rooms, cemeteries, hillside terraces, and a complex system of corridors within the four-square-kilometre area of the site. Storage structures were built within the confines of the enclosures that surround the largest *huacas,* and U-shaped structures occur in other enclosures. These features, plus the formal organization of the site into enclosures with restricted access, and zones of less formal, compact masonry structures, are strikingly similar to, but not identical with, Chimu architecture at Chan Chan.

The similarities between the architecture of Pampa Grande and that of Chan Chan — which will be described in some detail below — suggest that the Mochica probably had a social structure and a complementary economic system which, with certain modifications, were passed on to the Chimu. That the Incas, in their turn, adopted much of the Chimu social and religious structure demonstrates a continuity in Peruvian society for nearly a thousand years.

Chimu

The Chimu occupied the same area of the north coast

as the Mochica but established their capital at Chan Chan in the Moche valley. It is clear, however, from the distribution of Chimu ceramics and adobe architecture, that by A.D. 1470 (when the Incas conquered Chan Chan) the Chimu frontiers had been extended to embrace the central coast.

It has long been recognized that there was considerable cultural continuity between the Mochica and the Chimu, although the cultures were not identical. It is currently believed that the differences between Mochica and Chimu ceramic traits and architectural features were the result of an invasion of the coastal area by conquerors from the highlands about A.D. 900,[27] i.e., by the Huari, who had brought the Nazca culture to an end. Highland ceramics occur in abundance on the south coast and are frequently found on the central coast. On the north coast, however, highland ceramics are rare, and highland ceramic traits are attenuated or absent. Furthermore, the architectural features supposedly introduced by the highland invaders and developed by the Chimu (rectangular enclosures, "city" planning, use of stone masonry) all have Mochica precedents. It is probable, therefore, that the Mochica were the direct ancestors of the Chimu and that the more formalized Chimu architecture was patterned after the Mochica models. It

Carved wooden figure in a niche in the north entry of one of the large rectangular enclosures at Chan Chan.

is possible, too, that contact between the north coast and the highlands was a long-standing stable interrelationship and not the result of organized, short-term incursions in either direction.

When the Chimu established themselves at Chan Chan, they, like the inhabitants of Pampa Grande, chose a site which had not been occupied previously and began building a series of rectangular enclosures called *ciudadelas.* Eventually nine enclosures were built. Although they vary in size and interior details, each has three major internal divisions and all are oriented north-south. All *ciudadelas* have a single entrance in the centre of their north wall and a dog-leg corridor that leads to the northernmost interior division. Within this section there are plazas, tortuous corridors, patios with U-shaped structures (called portals in the description of the litter backrest, 237), and groups of storerooms. Much the same plan occurs in the central section, with three variations. Here there are fewer U-shaped structures, a greater number of storerooms, and, with one exception, a burial platform. The third section did not contain formally arranged structures, but it probably had flimsily built structures to house a service population. Large open wells occur in the *ciudadelas,* as well as in other enclosures at the site. These wells were excavated to tap

ground water, and some of them still contain clear water.[28]

On the west side of the site there is an extensive area of compact rooms which, in contrast to most of the more formal structures built of adobe, were constructed of stone masonry and plastered canes.

On the north side of the site there is a large boundary wall and a partially completed ditch. Beyond the wall and ditch are remains of field borders, fields with sinuous furrows, irrigation ditches, and a road. At the northern edge of the fields there is a large canal which formerly brought water from the Moche river and other sources to irrigate the fields. Amid the fields or along the large canal are small Chimu sites which share some of the formal architectural characteristics of Chan Chan and which probably were used as rural administrative centres during harvest, or as gathering points for the labour force which constructed and maintained the large canal.[29]

The number of *ciudadelas* at Chan Chan coincides with the number of Chimu kings mentioned by one of the early Spanish chroniclers. Since the *ciudadelas* are the most elaborate structures at Chan Chan and nearly all contain the heavily looted remains of a burial platform, it is believed that each was the palace of a king.

43

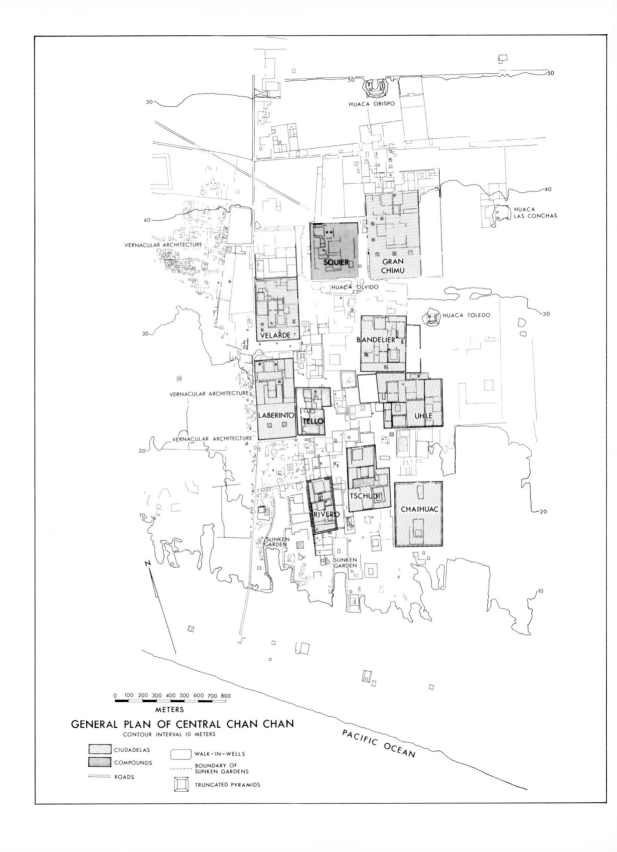

GENERAL PLAN OF CENTRAL CHAN CHAN

CONTOUR INTERVAL 10 METERS

CIUDADELAS

COMPOUNDS

ROADS

WALK-IN-WELLS

BOUNDARY OF
SUNKEN GARDENS

TRUNCATED PYRAMIDS

HUACA OBISPO

HUACA LAS CONCHAS

VERNACULAR ARCHITECTURE

SQUIER

GRAN CHIMU

HUACA OLVIDO

HUACA TOLEDO

VELARDE

BANDELIER

VERNACULAR ARCHITECTURE

LABERINTO

TELLO

UHLE

VERNACULAR ARCHITECTURE

TSCHUDI

RIVERO

CHAIHUAC

SUNKEN GARDEN

SUNKEN GARDEN

N

0 100 200 300 400 500 600 700 800

METERS

PACIFIC OCEAN

Aerial view of two of the large enclosures at Chan Chan, the
Chimu capital on the north coast of Peru.

Ruins of storerooms at Chan Chan.

The *ciudadelas* were also the centres for the concentration of wealth and the seats of economic control, as indicated by the great number of storerooms they contain.

Part of the labour force probably resided in the area of compact rooms on the west side of the site. The implements for weaving found in these ruins indicate that weaving was a common household task or one of several cottage industries.

There is also evidence of metalworking in the compact rooms. Stone hammers, polished and faceted stone pebbles, stone anvils, earthenware crucibles, and copper ore have been found here. Small copper objects (needles, digging stick tips, ornaments) have been found in the rooms, but very few if any objects of noble metals have been recovered.

The chroniclers who preserved the list of Chimu kings wrote that the Chimu were conquered by the Inca. After the conquest the last Chimu king, along with his court, artisans, and probably his property and treasury, was taken to Cuzco, the Inca capital.[30] This account is apparently accurate, because all of the excavated structures in *ciudadelas* at Chan Chan have proved to be empty, as if the entire site had been cleaned out by its last occupants or looted by the invaders. Since the Inca

valued textiles as one of the principal goods destined for state storage, it is probable that most of the storage in *ciudadelas* at Chan Chan contained this important material. Also, given the Inca identification of gold and silver with their divine kings, it is likely that the conquerors gathered up any gold or silver at Chan Chan for the enrichment of Inca palaces and temples. Other riches lay untouched in the burial platforms at Chan Chan until the Spanish began to mine them for treasure in the 16th century.

Although treasure hunting has continued uninterrupted at Chan Chan and some of the examples of Chimu metallurgy in major museums may have come from there, none of the pieces is well documented. Many of the objects in this exhibition, such as the gold poncho (136), the gloves (185, 186), the *tumi* (227), and the back-rest of the litter (237), are of Chimu design and were made between A.D. 1000 and 1470, perhaps at Chan Chan.

The few ethnohistoric references to the Chimu consistently mention that they had a rigidly structured social hierarchy and that their aristocrats were considered to have been created separately from commoners. Chimu kings were divine and were surrounded by noble courtiers who performed special functions or provided special

Ceramic representation of a U-shaped structure.

services.[31] Infractions of laws by commoners — primarily theft — were severely punished, and punishment was said to continue even after the death of the felon.

Archaeology has demonstrated that the Chimu built massive irrigation systems or extended earlier waterworks. They also cultivated several hundred more hectares of land in the Moche Valley than are worked today. Not only do these systems represent a certain aptitude for engineering, but they are the results of organized labour. A large investment of labour is also reflected in the manufacture of adobes and the construction of *ciudadelas,* massive earthworks, and *huacas.*

The amount of space devoted to storage in the *ciudadelas* and other adjacent enclosures, and the high walls around them, bear witness to the strict control over goods. The limited access system and the strategic location of U-shaped structures further demonstrate imperial control over the accumulation of wealth. The high walls and the tortuous corridor system that existed throughout the site were probably symbols of the separation of royalty from commoners and are evidence of the concern for security of imperial property.[32] It is likely, therefore, that the Chimu modified a social and economic system that had existed on the coast for several hundred years. Furthermore, it is believed that the Inca administrative

system and hierarchical social structure were adopted from the Chimu.[33] Because of this continuity from Mochica to Chimu to Inca, it is possible to interpret some aspects of Mochica and Chimu culture from our knowledge of the Inca.

Chancay

Before turning to the Inca, it is necessary to mention one local culture contemporary with Chimu, but centred on the central coast just north of modern Lima. Like Chimu, it is a culture of massive adobe walls and planned structures which, presumably, indicate a similar social organization. The pottery is distinctive — black on white — and is best characterized by large, hollow figurines, but for this exhibition the textiles and featherwork (247, 251, 252) and the unique funerary group (250) are of greatest importance.

The Inca and the Incas

"Inca" (lord) was a title reserved for the king who reigned in Cuzco. Since there is no generally accepted English term for the people ruled by the Inca except Inca or Incas, the plural form will be used here to distinguish the people from their king and the singular form to denote a distinctive cultural element or style of the period.

About A.D. 1200 the predecessors of the Incas were consolidating their control over the southern highlands of Peru. By 1400 they had overwhelmed a large part of the highlands by military conquest and were beginning to take control over part of the coast. During the time of imperial expansion, Inca Pachacuti organized a massive building effort at Cuzco, the site of his residence, seat of government, and devotional centre. In 1470 the Incas, under the leadership of General Yupanqui, were in direct contact with the Chimu and through excellent military tactics, ruse, or diplomacy quickly conquered Minchançaman, the last Chimu king at Chan Chan. Yupanqui became Inca soon after the conquest of the north coast, and during his reign Cuzco was further embellished, a hereditary aristocracy was probably established, and a complex administrative system was put into effect throughout the empire.[34]

Although problems of Inca royal succession were never completely resolved, the governmental system apparently functioned very well. Cuzco was the administrative capital, and other administrative centres were established throughout the empire. Members of the noble class and talented subjects were chosen as admin-istrators in principal centres beyond Cuzco. Rural administration was left in the hands of local authorities, once it was determined that they were loyal to the Inca. The government penetrated all levels of social organization and was concentrated in the divine presence of the Inca himself.

Inca economic organization was based on privilege, service, reciprocity, and labour. There was no standard medium of exchange, and markets (with the possible exception of occasional rural markets) did not exist. Private property, as we understand it, was probably unknown, even though the nobility controlled the largest quantity of goods and the Inca distributed or retained lands.

At the local level, farmers cultivated fields allotted to them by the Inca as adult, married members of a community. Production from these fields stayed in the community, but community members were obliged to work on the Inca's land or on the properties assigned to the official religion in exchange for land grants and the services of the Inca as an earthly divinity. The products from the fields of the Inca and the church were destined for the royal court, for military installations, and for the maintenance of the priesthood. Local administra-tive authorities managed the distribution of land and

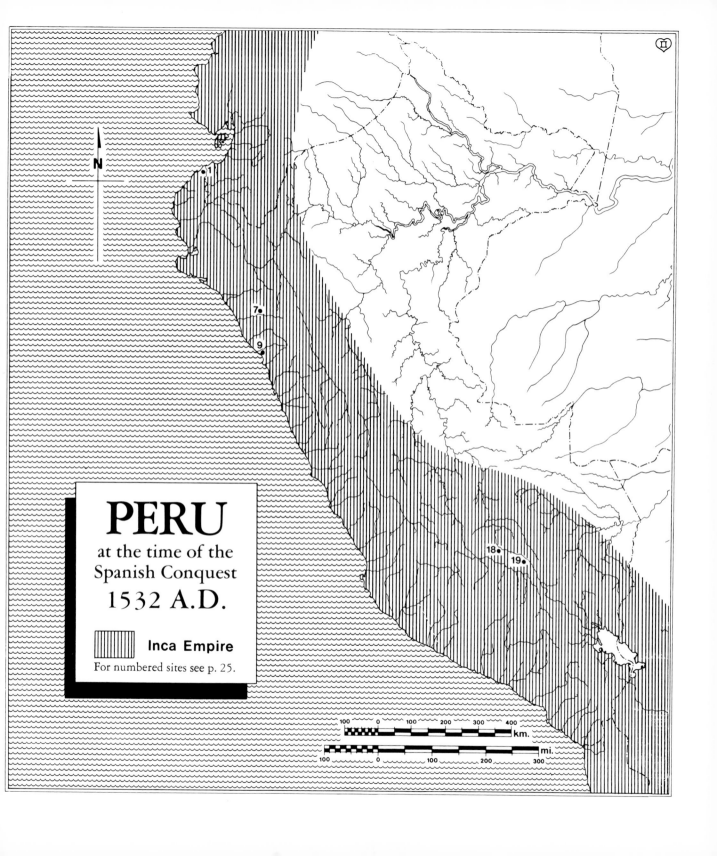

PERU

at the time of the
Spanish Conquest

1532 A.D.

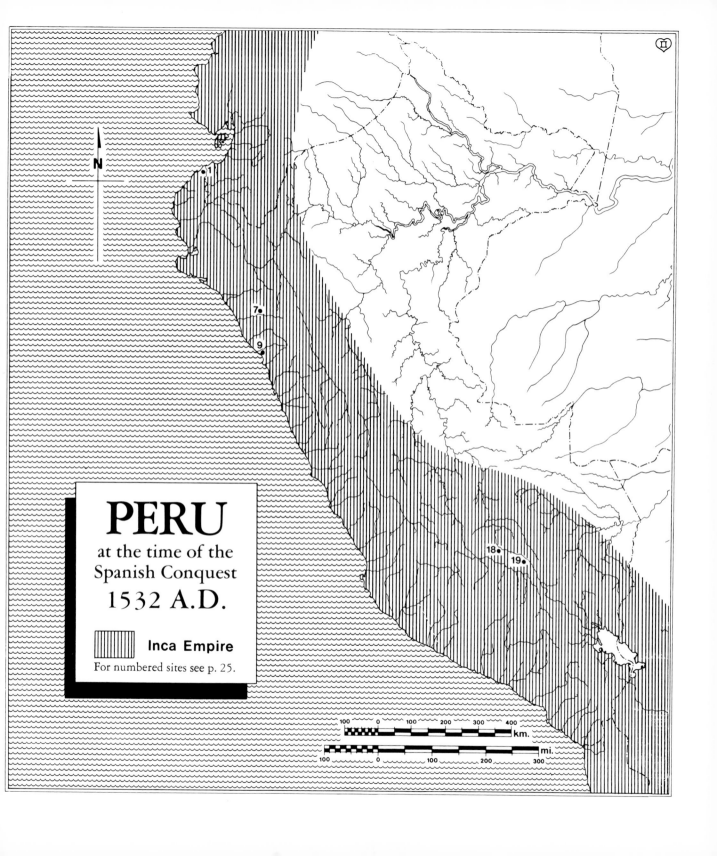 Inca Empire

For numbered sites see p. 25.

organized labour for the construction and maintenance of public projects (canals, irrigation ditches, public buildings, etc.) and for the cultivation of Inca and church fields. The local administrators probably received some produce from Inca lands, but their major recompense consisted of personal service from the local population. The labourers who did the agricultural work or provided services to administrators or to the church received food, drink, and fiestas for their tasks. In essence, the workers provided their time in exchange for access to a plot of land, land that devolved to the Inca or to the church if the labourer died, or when the community had no further need or ability to cultivate that land.

The tasks assigned to the members of a community were based on the number of able-bodied men in the community. If the number was small, the task was probably adjusted accordingly. On major projects like the excavation of a canal or the construction of a public building, large numbers of labourers were assembled, but groups within the labour pool probably varied in size. Perhaps these smaller groups lost their identity within the mass, but they must have been accounted for in order to meet their community obligation and to receive their food and drink. This problem was overcome, apparently, by the Inca census system and by the assignment of foremen to supervise different-sized groups within the general work force.

Textiles played an important role in the Inca economy. Wealth was measured by the number of llamas or alpacas in Inca, church, and community herds. Most wool was reserved for high-ranking groups. The wool was woven as a labour obligation, and the finest textiles were always destined for noble storerooms or for the use of the aristocracy. Textiles made of vicuña wool were restricted to the exclusive use of the Inca. Coarser and more common textiles woven from community herds or cotton from the coast stayed in the community for internal use and distribution. Common cloth produced from Inca and church herds and fields went into storage for use by the army or the church. Textiles from government stores were probably distributed in times of stress or provided to labourers who worked on government projects.[35] In any event, mass production of food and textiles was essential to the maintenance of the Inca social and economic structure, and this production depended upon the organization of labour and access to arable land.

The Inca had exclusive access to gold and silver, probably as symbols of his divine status rather than as commodities of intrinsic economic value.[36] Since the

Inca was the head of the state as well as of the church, other cult objects such as certain shells (*Spondylus* sp., spiny oyster) and gems (emeralds and amethysts) were within his jurisdiction. Of these, only amethyst is native to Peru, and it is probable that even much of this was imported from adjacent countries. *Spondylus* shells were used in large numbers and may have been supplied by maritime traders, who were the only merchants in prehistoric Peru.[37] These shells occur at archaeological sites in the highlands and on the coast continuously from Chavin times. Apparently there was never a time in Peruvian prehistory when the source of these shells, the closest of which is in Ecuador, was under Peruvian control.

Besides gold, silver, and ubiquitous copper, the Incas probably began to smelt tin and add it to copper to form bronze. The scarcity of Inca objects in the precious metals in this exhibition, as well as in other private and public collections throughout the world, is a direct result of the Spanish conquest and the systematic looting of all available pieces for immediate conversion into bullion.

The first European to enter Peru was probably Alejo García, a Spanish adventurer who came into contact with the Incas about 1520. It has been suggested that Huayna Capac, one of the last Inca emperors, died from smallpox, which had somehow entered Peru shortly before the Spanish arrived but after Europeans had landed in Central America.[38]

On his second voyage of exploration from Panama, Francisco Pizarro landed briefly near Tumbes on the far north coast of Peru in 1528. He returned to Panama and, on his third voyage south, landed at Tumbes once again on May 1, 1532. Along with a troop of 62 mounted men and 102 infantry armed with crossbows, a few muskets, and two small cannon, Pizarro began his march south along the coast and turned inland up the Zaña and Jequetepeque valleys towards the highlands.

The rapid collapse of the Inca empire before a handful of Spanish soldiers has always intrigued historians. The reasons are various, but two, at least, are very important. The political situation in Peru at the time of the Spanish landing was confused; a civil war between the legitimate Inca Huascar and his half-brother rival, Atahualpa, was just being resolved, for Huascar had been captured by Atahualpa. The political disarray of the empire and Atahualpa's uncertainty as to the intentions of the Spanish played into the hands of Pizarro, and he exploited the situation to the utmost.

On November 15, 1532, the Spanish were in sight of Cajamarca, a major Inca town in the northern highlands. By coincidence, the new Inca Atahualpa was nearby and within a few days arrived in Cajamarca. Immediately, he and his retinue were ambushed, most of his retainers killed, and Atahualpa taken captive. The Spanish demanded a ransom in gold. Atahualpa not only turned over what gold there was in Cajamarca but ordered that gold and silver be brought from the southern capital of Cuzco. As the gold and silver began to accumulate in Cajamarca, it became clear to the Spanish that an immense treasure was at their fingertips. A few years ago, when gold cost $35 an ounce, it was estimated that the value of the precious metal brought to Cajamarca as Atahualpa's ransom was over $8,000,000.[39] If valued at $100 an ounce, that same quantity of gold would be worth about $23,000,000.

That much wealth, delivered at the command of one man, no doubt made the Spanish realize that more gold was probably available elsewhere and that they must assume that man's power in order to get it. Within a few months Atahualpa's ransom was paid in full, but despite the payment and the fact that he eventually accepted conversion to Christianity, Atahualpa was killed. Instead of being burned as a pagan, Atahualpa — as a Christian gentleman — was garrotted against a post in the central square of Cajamarca on August 29, 1533.

The Spanish marched on to Cuzco and reached the Inca capital one year after entering Cajamarca. There they found more gold, some of it apparently as wide metal bands affixed to buildings, gardens of gold and silver, and golden altar ornaments in the Temple of the Sun. Although a few objects were sent to the Spanish court, nearly everything made of silver and gold was melted down.

By the time Cuzco was looted, the Spanish probably had doubled the amount of precious metal in their possession. Within about eighteen months of their landing, Pizarro, his men, and the King of Spain had divided about $70,000,000's worth of gold and silver, and Peru was theirs.

The gold in this exhibit was never part of that treasure. But some of Atahualpa's ransom or other Peruvian gold and silver melted down by the Spanish is undoubtedly in bank vaults throughout the world, and a fraction of it is being worn as jewellery by visitors to this exhibition.

Notes

1. John H. Rowe, "Inca Culture at the Time of the Spanish Conquest", *Handbook of South American Indians,* ed. Julian H. Steward, Bureau of American Ethnology, Bulletin 143, II (Wash-

ington, D.C.: Smithsonian Institution, 1946) pp. 183 ff. (hereafter Rowe, "Inca Culture"). John V. Murra, "Cloth and Its Functions in the Inca State", *American Anthropologist,* vol. 64 (1962), pp. 710 ff. (hereafter Murra, "Cloth").

2. Georg Petersen, "Mineria y Metalurgia en el Antiguo Peru", *Arqueologicas,* vol. 12 (1970).

3. Rowe, "Inca Culture". Gordon R. Willey, *An Introduction to American Archaeology,* vol. 2, *South America* (Englewood Cliffs, N.J.: Prentice-Hall, 1971) (hereafter Willey, *South America*).

4. Robert E. Bell, *Archaeological Investigations at the Site of El Inca, Ecuador* (Quito: Editorial Casa de la Cultura Ecuatoriana, 1965). Junius Bird, "Antiquity and Migrations of the Early Inhabitants of Patagonia", *The Geographical Review,* vol. 28 (1938), pp. 250 ff. Jose Emperaire, Annette Laming-Emperaire, and Henri Reichlen, "La grotte Fell et autres sites de la région volcanique de la Patagonie chilienne", *Journal de la Société des Américanistes,* tome 52 (1963), pp. 167 ff. Richard S. MacNeish, *Second Annual Report of the Ayacucho Archaeological-Botanical Project* (Phillips Academy, Andover, Mass.: Robert S. Peabody Foundation for Archaeology, 1969) (hereafter MacNeish, *Ayacucho II*).

5. MacNeish, *Ayacucho II*. Rogger Ravines, "Secuencia y Cambios en los artefactos liticos del sur del Peru", *Revista del Museo Nacional,* tomo 38 (1972), pp. 131 ff.

6. Paul P. Ossa and Michael E. Moseley, "La Cumbre: a Preliminary Report on Research into the Early Lithic Occupation of the Moche Valley, Peru", *Nawpa Pacha,* no. 9 (1971), pp. 1 ff.

7. Edward P. Lanning, *Peru Before the Incas* (Englewood Cliffs, N.J.: Prentice-Hall, 1967) (hereafter Lanning, *Peru*). Michael E. Moseley, *The Maritime Foundations of Andean Civilization*

(Menlo Park, Cal.: Cummings Publishing Co., 1975) (hereafter Moseley, *Maritime Foundations*).

8. Thomas F. Lynch, "Preceramic Transhumance in the Callejon de Huaylas, Peru", *American Antiquity,* vol. 36 (1971), pp. 139 ff.

9. Moseley, *Maritime Foundations*.

10. Lanning, *Peru*. Moseley, *Maritime Foundations*. Willey, *South America*.

11. Moseley, *Maritime Foundations*.

12. Frederic Engel, "Le Complexe Precéramique d'El Paraiso (Perou)", *Journal de la Société des Americanistes,* tome 55 (1967), pp. 43 ff.

13. Engel, *op. cit.* Moseley, *Maritime Foundations*.

14. Betty J. Meggers, Clifford Evans, and Emilio Estrada, *Early Formative Period of Coastal Ecuador,* Smithsonian Institution Contributions to Anthropology, vol. 1 (Washington, D.C.: Smithsonian Institution, 1965). James A. Ford, *A Comparison of Formative Cultures in the Americas: Diffusion or the Psychic Unity of Man?,* Smithsonian Institution Contributions to Anthropology, vol. 11 (Washington, D.C.: Smithsonian Institution, 1969).

15. Gerardo Reichel-Dolmatoff, *Colombia* (New York: Praeger, 1965). Donald W. Lathrap, *The Upper Amazon* (London: Thames and Hudson, 1970).

16. Donald W. Lathrap, "The Tropical Forest and the Cultural Context of Chavin", *Dumbarton Oaks Conference on Chavin,* ed. E. P. Benson (Washington: Dumbarton Oaks Research Laboratory and Collection, 1971).

17. David H. Kelley and Duccio Bonavia, "New Evidence for

Preceramic Maize on the Coast of Peru", *Nawpa Pacha,* no. 1 (1963), pp. 39 ff.

18. Luis G. Lumbreras, *The Peoples and Cultures of Ancient Peru,* trans. Betty J. Meggers (Washington, D.C.: Smithsonian Institution Press, 1974. John H. Rowe, *Chavin Art, an Inquiry into Its Form and Meaning* (New York: Museum of Primitive Art, 1962).

19. B. Duccio Bonavia, *Ricchata Quellccani: Pinturas Murales Prehispanicas* (Lima: Banco Industrial, 1974).

20. Rafael Larco Hoyle, *Los Mochicas* (Lima: Casa editoria "La Cronica" y "Variedades", 1938).

21. Bonavia, *op. cit.*

22. Thomas C. Patterson, *America's Past: A New World Archaeology* (Glenview, Illinois: Scott, Foresman, 1973).

23. Maria Reiche, *Mystery on the Desert* (Stuttgart: 1968); and "Giant Ground-Drawings on the Peruvian Desert", *Verhandlungen* of the 38th International Congress of Americanists, Munich (1969), vol. 1, pp. 379 ff. Loren McIntyre, "Mystery of the Ancient Nazca Lines", *National Geographic Magazine,* vol. 147, no. 5 (May 1975), pp. 716 ff.

24. C. M. Hastings and Michael E. Moseley, "The Adobes of Huaca del Sol and Huaca de la Luna", *American Antiquity,* vol 40 (1975), pp. 196 ff.

25. Michael E. Moseley, "Prehistoric Principles of Labor Organization in the Moche Valley, Peru", *American Antiquity,* vol. 40 (1975), pp. 191 ff.

26. Bonavia, *op. cit.*

27. Richard P. Schaedel, "Incipient Urbanization and Seculariza-tion in Tiahuanacoid Peru", *American Antiquity,* vol. 31 (1966), pp. 338 ff.

28. Kent C. Day, "Walk-in Wells and Water Management at Chan Chan, Peru", *The Rise and Fall of Civilizations: An Archaeological Reader,* ed. J. A. Sabloff and C. C. Lamberg-Karlovsky (Menlo Park, California: Cummings, 1974), pp. 182 ff.

29. Michael E. Moseley, personal communication, 1975.

30. John H. Rowe, "The Kingdom of Chimor", *Acta Americana,* vol. VI (1948), pp. 26 ff. (hereafter Rowe, "Chimor").

31. Miguel Cabello de Balboa, *Miscelanea antartica: una historia del Peru antiquo por Miguel Cabello Valboa* [1586] (Lima: Universidad Nacional Mayor de San Marcos, Instituto de Etnologia, 1951). Rowe, "Chimor".

32. Kent C. Day, *The Architecture of Ciudadelas Rivero, Chan Chan, Peru* (Harvard University Ph.D. dissertation, unpublished, 1973).

33. Rowe, "Chimor"

34. Rowe, "Inca Culture".

35. Murra, "Cloth".

36. Rowe, "Inca Culture".

37. Maria Rostworowski de Diez Canseco, "Mercaderes del valle de Chincha en la epoca prehispanica", *Estudios Americanos,* vol. 5 (Seville: Universidad de Sevilla, 1952), pp. 135 ff.

38. Rowe, "Inca Culture".

39. Samuel K. Lothrop, *Inca Treasure as Depicted by Spanish Historians* (Los Angeles: Southwest Museum [Frederick Webb Hodge Anniversary Publication Fund, vol. 2], 1938).

Metallurgy
A. D. Tushingham

Example of a small prehistoric furnace. The draught for this type of furnace was supplied by the wind.

To the best of our knowledge, gold was the first metal to be worked in Peru. Fragments of gold foil and an early goldsmith's set of stone anvil and hammers have been found at a site in the south-central highlands of Peru dating from about 1500 B.C.[1] By the Chavin period, sophisticated techniques had been developed for alloying gold with silver and copper to produce sheets with gold or silver surfaces by the *mise en couleur* method, and for welding and soldering these pieces together.[2] From about the same period, or a little later, hammered copper tools are known from the south coast of Peru. Bronze, the alloy of copper and tin, was made in Peru, but there is some question whether it was made in any quantity before the Spanish conquest.[3] Platinum was known prehistorically in South America, but its use was apparently limited to the northern Andean area near its sources in Ecuador and Colombia. Small lead objects were made in Peru as early as A.D. 600–800, and lead was used as an inlay in wooden or other metal objects during the time of the Incas. Iron was also known to the Incas, but only in the form of meteoric iron, haematite, and perhaps magnetite. A piece of low-grade iron ore has been found at a late Mochica site, but there is no evidence that any of the iron compounds were smelted prehistorically in Peru or elsewhere in the New World. Mercury and cinnabar were known to the Incas and cinnabar was used earlier as a pigment.

Gold was probably originally obtained as nuggets in rivers and streams and in the outwash from melting glaciers high in the Andes (see 1–4). This type of placer mining was facilitated at times by heaping up boulders in dry stream beds; when the rivers were in spate, the particles of gold washed downstream would be caught in the grain and crevices of the boulders and removed when the water abated.[4]

It is clear, however, from the amount of gold used in ornaments and in the official cult, and deposited in large quantities in tombs, that the metal must have been mined intensively from a comparatively early date — perhaps as early as the turn of the Christian era. The means by which the other metallic ores were extracted are not known in detail, but success in the mining of gold could lead to similar methods for the extraction of silver and copper ores.

Some of the early Spanish chroniclers noted, for example, that the native people in what is now Bolivia smelted ores in small furnaces built on hillsides. The furnaces were stocked with charcoal and wood as fuel, and the draught was supplied by strong late-afternoon and evening winds. In another case, metalworkers in

On the left, two men blow into a fire to smelt metal. On the right, a man is seated on a large flat stone (a batan*) in the act of hammering a lump of metal with a stone in his right hand. After M. Jeronimo Benzoni,* La Historia del Mundo Nuevo *[1572]. Translated into Castilian and annotated by Carlos Radicati di Primeglio (Lima: Universidad de San Marcos, 1967), fig. opp. p. 62.*

Quito made a crucible of earthenware and pulverized charcoal, filled it with ore, and placed it in a fire. Then they blew through canes into the fire to increase its intensity and smelt the metal from the ore.

Although there are plenty of hillsides and constant afternoon and evening winds on the Peruvian coast, no hillside smelters have been found there. Structures at Chan Chan, the Chimu capital, which were once identified as smelters are merely areas of buildings which burned with such intense heat that their earthen floors and walls fused and left a deposit of very crude glass. This melted earth has been called slag, but it contains no higher concentration of metal than nearby unburned soil. No evidence of portable furnaces or special hearths has been found at any Chimu or Mochica site as yet. However, fragments of small earthenware crucibles, some with gobbets of copper adhering to them, have been found in domestic or mortuary contexts at Chimu and a few Mochica sites. The evidence of these few crucibles has recently been enhanced by the discovery of a Mochica bowl of about A.D. 600, which apparently depicts a furnace in which smelting is being carried on with the aid of draughts produced by men blowing through tubes.[5]

By whatever means the smelting was accomplished,

the yield from each furnace, hearth, or crucible was probably a few small lumps of metal which varied in composition. In fact, nearly all Peruvian metals were alloys. This fact, as well as the recognition that the alloys were usually intentional, and the discovery within the last five years of the methods used by the Peruvian metallurgists have initiated a whole new series of studies into pre-Columbian metalworking.[6]

The natural or artificial alloying of metals had one direct benefit: the lowering of the melting point. It is obvious that early metalworkers could not heat their furnaces to the critical temperatures required to melt silver ($1,420°$C), copper ($1,083°$C), or gold ($1,063°$C). The mixture of two or more metals, however, substantially reduced these temperatures. Furthermore, the quantity and durability of the noble metals were extended or enhanced by the addition of copper. Chemical analysis of samples of Peruvian silver shows that it was always alloyed with copper, and occasionally with some gold. Many gold objects are an alloy of gold, silver, and copper. The proportions of metals in the alloys vary greatly from piece to piece and are seldom uniform even in a single piece. These differences are probably the result of the smiths' having mixed or re-melted several batches of alloys.

56

A Mochica bowl apparently depicting a
smelting operation. From a private
collection in Lima, Peru. Photograph
courtesy of C. B. Donnan.

Objects of relatively pure gold and silver — mostly small — do occur in Peru, but the larger pieces, made up from sheet metal by hammering and embossing, are just as clearly often heavily alloyed with other metals. Moreover, such alloys are not merely natural admixtures but have been artificially created as a stage in the metallurgical process. Examination of thin sections of the sheet metal has demonstrated the methods of working the sheet itself, and how the silver or gold surface was produced. It appears that the metallic mixture was poured into thin slabs or ingots which were then worked, by alternate hammering and annealing (heating), down to the required thickness of 0.2 mm or less. We may hazard the suggestion that the large discs of metal from Vicus, represented by two specimens in the exhibition (5, 6), represent the form of ingots at that period. Some twenty-five or thirty of these discs are preserved in the Museo "Oro del Peru"; they average 3–4 mm in thickness and have diameters averaging about 40 cm. Their surfaces, without analysis, suggest the presence of gold, silver, and copper. Much smaller ingots (e.g., 3, 4) may represent the size and form of a later period.[7]

To produce a sheet of silver — that is, a sheet with silver surfaces — the Peruvian metalworker began with an ingot of silver and copper. Beating the metal would make it hard and brittle, a condition that was removed by annealing. During the annealing process, the copper within the alloy moved to the surface, where it became oxidized. The resultant dark scale of copper oxide was dissolved by pickling the metal, i.e., by the application of a mild acid; for the Peruvian metalworker this might well have been urine, but acetic acid or other available acids from fruits or leaves could also have been used. When the oxide was removed, the process of hammering and annealing would be repeated. As the copper was gradually removed from the alloy near the surface of the sheet, the silver was left. The thinner the sheet became, the more frequently was annealing required, but the thicker became the enriched surface layer of silver.

The same principle was applied to the production of a sheet of metal with gold surfaces. The alloy required for this contained copper, silver, and gold (the last often in small quantities).[8] The repeated hammering and annealing of a sheet of this alloy produced, first, a sheet with an enriched layer of silver at the surface. (It is this silver that appears on some objects when the gold surface is worn away.) To obtain a gold surface, the metalworker had to remove some of the silver, just as he removed copper from the copper/silver alloy to obtain a sheet with a silver surface. The stronger acids, such as nitric

58

and sulphuric acid, required to remove the silver and used by Old World metalworkers in a similar technique called *mise en couleur,* were not available to the pre-Columbian Indians of America. Experiments in the laboratory, however, have demonstrated that simple substances easily available to them could be used to produce the necessary corrosive effect. Some clay soils along the Peruvian coast contain significant amounts of potassium nitrate and sulphates of potassium, copper, and iron. It is likely that the coastal metallurgists mixed salitre, a soil with a high concentration of potassium nitrate, with alum, common salt, and water to make a paste. This was applied to the silvered surface of the metal and perhaps heated to accelerate the corrosion. When the paste was removed and the sheet washed, the thin black scale left on the surface was removed with a hot and strong solution of common salt. Burnishing, or moderate heating to consolidate the gold particles on the surface, produced a smooth, shiny gold finish. The operation could, of course, be repeated several times to build up a thicker layer of gold.[9] The process of producing a silver or gold surface by a method of hammering, annealing, and pickling is now generally called "depletion gilding".

It is true, of course, that if the silver or gold surface was thin, serious problems could arise. The corrosion of the silver, and particularly of the copper, in the alloy could cause eruptions through the surface. There is, for instance, little trace of gold on the obverse of mask no. 54; here the corrosion products of copper and silver appear very heavy. The reverse, however, shows much more of the gold preserved. The spider (59) and mask (57) have been similarly affected. The small circular plaque (60) has apparently lost all of its original gold surface. So serious is the corrosion, in many cases, that it is virtually impossible, without careful examination, to discover whether the object originally had a gold, silver, or copper surface. Good examples are the breast-plates (364, 365), which appear to be made of copper or bronze; nevertheless, the gleam of gold here and there suggests strongly that the original surface was gold and that the present green surface is the result of the corrosion of copper which has broken through from the basic alloy.

On the basis of this new discovery of the methods by which the ancient Peruvian metallurgists produced sheets with gold and silver surfaces, we may make conjectures about the manufacture of objects which appear to be made of the two metals fused together. The best examples are the nose ornaments from Vicus (e.g., 22, 32, 37, 38, 42). These have not been examined scientifically but, if the production of a gold surface on top of a silver surface depended only on the application of a corrosive paste, it would seem a very slight step to "parcel depletion gilding", that is, the differential treatment of the surface by the application of the paste to part of the sheet only so as to produce a silver finish and a gold finish side by side. It seems clear, also, that where there is embossing (e.g., 22, 42) this operation was carried out after the silver surface had been produced (for otherwise the hammering and annealing would destroy it) but before the corrosive paste was applied to produce the gold surface.

There are, of course, other cases (e.g., the *tumis*, 227, 234) where the effect of juxtaposed gold and silver appears to have been obtained mechanically by laying a thin layer of gold foil over the silver to produce a sort of checkerboard effect. Unfortunately, it is not possible, before this catalogue goes to the printer, to make the tests which would, in some cases at least, demonstrate which method was used to produce the desired effect.

Metalworking in Peru was essentially a sheet-metal technique, accomplished by cutting and manipulating two-dimensional sheets to produce the objects and forms desired. The processes were embossing, beating into a mould, chasing, and burnishing, all of which could be carried out with simple tools. A selection of worked stones, intended to be used as anvils or hammers for a variety of purposes, is included in this exhibition (7–18).[10] With such tools a craftsman could produce anything from pins and needles to the large funerary masks of the Chimu period.

True three-dimensional objects without seams (the beaker cups, bowls, and jars, 51, 52, 92, 93, 144–46, 198–202, and 207, are good examples) were created by raising, that is, by hammering the gold sheet on a horizontal arm or stake in a progressive series of concentric circles, working outward and upward from base to rim. Repeated blows of the hammer, however, would make the gold brittle and unworkable, a result that could be reversed by annealing to bring the gold back to its natural malleability. A process of alternate hammerings and annealings would finally produce the shape desired. A final hammering would provide a hardness and toughness proof against easy damage. Burnishing, as a last step, would remove the hammer marks.

Production of more complex forms required the development of techniques for joining individually shaped pieces together. The obvious method is simply a mechanical one — the use of rivets, staples, or clamps inserted through holes punched or bored in the overlapped edges. Examples of such a technique are very common (223, 235, 244, etc.; see also the attachment of spangles and other ornaments, 57, 94, 228, etc.). More sophisticated methods, however, were also applied, even from a very early period. The jaguar (19) employs very interesting welding and soldering techniques that have only recently been recognized and appreciated.[6] There is little doubt that soldering was used in the manufacture of the thousands of hollow gold beads (e.g., 282, 323, 324, 332), which were made in at least two parts and later joined together; in the securing of wire to sheet (59, 65, 66, 87, 88, 96, 101, etc.); and in the assembly of the many parts of complex objects (such as 162 and 205). Whether welding was also used in the later period cannot be demonstrated from objects in the present exhibition, simply bcause no tests have yet been made to discover the methods employed, but it would be strange if such a process, known for nearly 2,000 years, should not have continued to be used.

Variations in the colour of the gold in masks and other pieces are due to differences in the amount of copper, silver, and other impurities present. Colour tones among the pieces range from pale greenish to yellow and reddish-brown, depending upon the alloy.

The miniature gold masks worn by figures mounted on the litter back-rest (237) show extensive painting, particularly with a thick red paint. Parts of these small masks were covered with pieces of leather to which feathers were glued. The large masks have traces of red, blue, white, and green paint on cheeks and eyes. It is apparent from both the miniature and the large masks that most of the gold was a foundation for bright paint or colourful featherwork. Shell appliqués sometimes cover the eyes of masks, while precious and semi-precious stones mark the pupils or depend from wires fixed in the pupils. Except for the area around the mouth, therefore, very little of the gold was left visible once the masks were finished and worn by the living or placed over the faces of the dead.

Our discussion of Peruvian metallurgy has been confined, so far, to work in sheet metal. The only reference to casting has been in the production of "ingots" of copper/silver or copper/silver/gold alloys which formed the raw material that the metalworker hammered and annealed to produce the sheet from which objects could be made. It has been generally assumed, however, that the *cire perdue* ("lost-wax") process of casting was used in Peru. That it was so used, at least in Inca times and for the production of bronze castings, seems certain. Even if beeswax was not obtainable (the native stingless bees of Peru produce little or none[11]), tallow, resin, and other available substances could have been used. There seems little doubt that the process was known to the metalworkers of Mexico at the time of the Spanish Conquest, and the inference has been drawn that this process, along with metallurgy in general, was derived by them from South America. While this may well be true, it does not follow that the process had its origins in Peru. We can only say that if the attribution of such pieces as 83, 84, 85, 86, 87, 88, 90, 91, 96, and 100 to Frias in the Mujica Gallo catalogue[12] is correct (and there seems no reason to doubt it), and if they were made by the *cire perdue* method, the art of *gold* casting was known in Peru soon after the beginning of the Christian era. Strangely, the evidence of its use in the later cultures of Peru — at least insofar as the material in the present exhibition provides a fair sampling of them — is rather sparse until we reach late pre-Inca or Inca times (the pins 125 and 126, attributed to Nazca, may be exceptions). Possibly, the introduction of bronze into Peru brought with it the technique of *cire perdue* casting, so reviving an art which had almost died out.

As a craft, metallurgy was practised in Peru for the production of utilitarian copper objects like digging stick tips, needles, pins, and spindle whorls. Copper was also fashioned into a large variety of ornamental objects worn as jewellery or sewn to clothing and head ornaments. Human bones have been found in graves, stained green from oxidized copper objects which have long since disappeared. A green stain on finger and wrist bones is presumably evidence for rings and bracelets; if on ribs and sternums, we must probably assume copper necklaces or pectorals. A green stain on skulls suggests copper head-bands, crowns, or masks. Semilunar *tumi* knives have also been found with burials.

Next to copper, gold objects are the most common metallic materials recovered from tombs. Presumably the tombs enriched with gold were those of high-status individuals who were probably divine kings during their lifetimes. Silver is seldom found because it, like copper, disintegrates rapidly. Silver objects were also probably included in high-status graves, but it is not known if silver offerings were placed with certain individuals or randomly mixed with gold pieces.

It is clear that gold and silver objects were highly esteemed and enjoyed a special status among the Peruvians. These metals were probably considered sacred and were identified with celestial deities. Both the sun and the moon were principal deities of the Incas and the earlier coastal peoples. The Incas, however, placed greater emphasis upon the primacy of the sun, while the coastal peoples believed the moon was the greater deity of the two. In the case of the Incas, the Inca himself was identified as representative of the solar god, and gold, the symbol of the sun, was reserved for the Inca and the cult of the sun. With the exception of the coastal emphasis upon the divine importance of the moon, it is likely that the Incas adopted most of the ideology and the status symbols of the coastal peoples after they conquered the Chimu. Therefore the Incas were the last inheritors of a long tradition of divine kings, many of whom took their golden and silver symbols of divinity to their graves. As the earth yielded up more gold and silver to be laboured over and crafted by common men, the next divine king was vested with his proper, sacrosanct adornments.

Notes

1. Joel W. Grossman, "An Ancient Gold Worker's Tool Kit: the Earliest Metal Technology in Peru", *Archaeology,* vol. 25, no. 4 (October 1972), pp. 270 ff.

2. Samuel K. Lothrop, "Gold Ornaments of Chavin Style from Chongoyape, Peru", *American Antiquity,* vol. VI (1940-41), pp. 250 ff.; "Gold Artifacts of Chavin Style", *American Antiquity,* vol. XVI (1950-51), pp. 226 ff. Allen Wardwell, *The Gold of Ancient America* (Museum of Fine Arts, Boston; Art Institute of Chicago, Chicago; Virginian Museum of Fine Arts, Richmond: 1968), pp. 16 ff. See further, note 6.

3. Some South American archaeologists, however, believe that bronze was made in Bolivia and Peru as early as A.D. 300–500 and came into widespread use, particularly for weapons, by A.D. 900. See L. G. Lumbreras, *Las Fundaciones de Huamanca* (Lima: 1974), pp. 119 ff. At least some of the "bronze" objects ascribed to the Mochica are a copper-arsenic alloy, not a copper-tin alloy.

4. Samuel K. Lothrop, *Inca Treasure as Depicted by Spanish Historians* (Los Angeles: Southwest Museum [Frederick Webb Hodge Anniversary Publication Funds, vol. 2.], 1938).

5. For a summary of documentary and archaeological evidence on Peruvian smelting methods, see Christopher B. Donnan, "A Precolumbian Smelter from Northern Peru", *Archaeology,* vol. 26, no. 4 (October 1973), pp. 289 ff.

6. See Heather N. Lechtman, "Ancient Methods of Gilding Silver: Examples from the Old and the New Worlds", *Science and Archaeology,* ed. Robert H. Brill (Cambridge, Mass.: Massachusetts Institute of Technology Press, 1971), pp. 2 ff.; and "The Gilding of Metals in Precolumbian Peru", *The Application of Science in*

Examination of Works of Art, ed. William J. Young (Boston: Museum of Fine Arts, 1973), pp. 38 ff. Heather Lechtman, Lee A. Parsons, and William J. Young, *Seven Matched Hollow Gold Jaguars from Peru's Early Horizon,* Studies in Pre-Columbian Art & Archaeology, no. 16 (Washington, D.C.: Dumbarton Oaks, Trustees for Harvard University, 1975). The description of ancient Peruvian metallurgical methods given here draws directly on these pioneering studies.

7. Donnan, *op. cit.,* pp. 293 ff.

8. See Lechtman, "The Gilding of Metals . . .", p. 39, where nine samples vary from 7.2% to 41.6%.

9. Where this was not done, the thin coating of gold — little more than a wash — might not be continuous and could easily be worn away, giving that ambiguous surface which is difficult to describe as "gold" or "silver".

10. For a group of similar tools now in the Peabody Museum, Harvard University, see S. K. Lothrop, "Metalworking Tools from the Central Coast of Peru", *American Antiquity,* vol. XVI (1950-51), pp. 160 ff.; for very early examples from Peru see Grossman, *op. cit.,* pp. 274 ff. Stone moulds, similar to 363 (which is probably of the Colonial period), could have been used to shape a series of identical embossed forms.

11. Junius Bird, "Treasures from the Land of Gold", *Art in Virginia,* vol. 8 (1967).

12. Miguel Mujica Gallo, *Catalogue. Museum Gold of Peru* (Lima: Miguel Mujica Gallo Foundation, 1970).

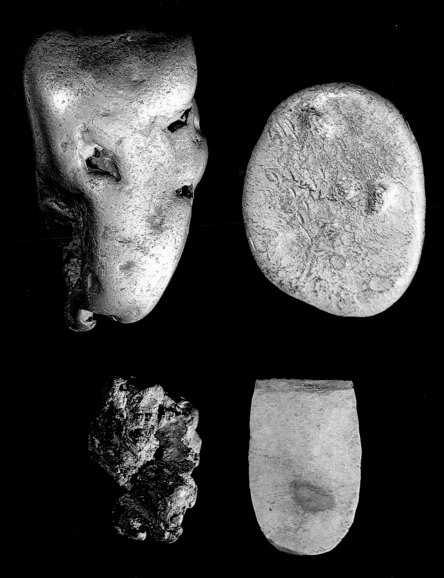

1-4

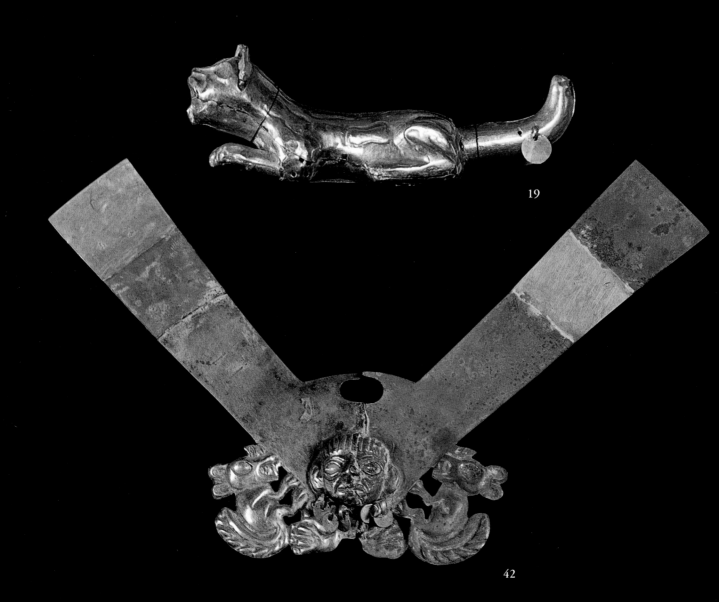

19

42

53

74

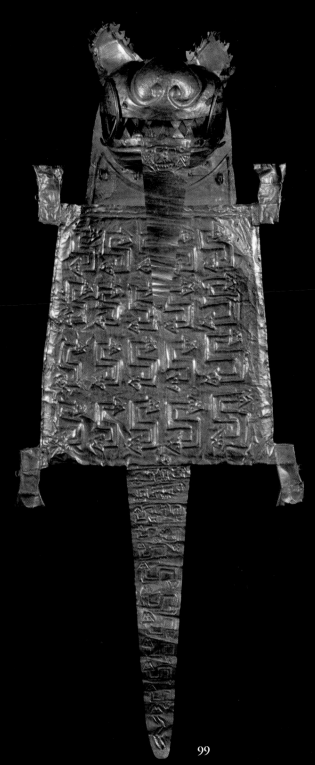

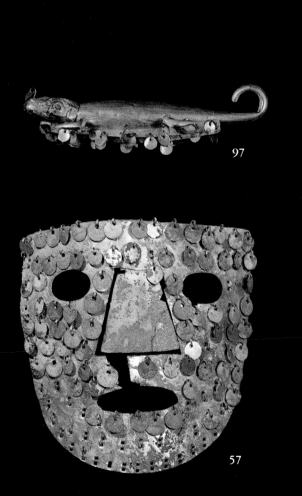

97

57

58

99

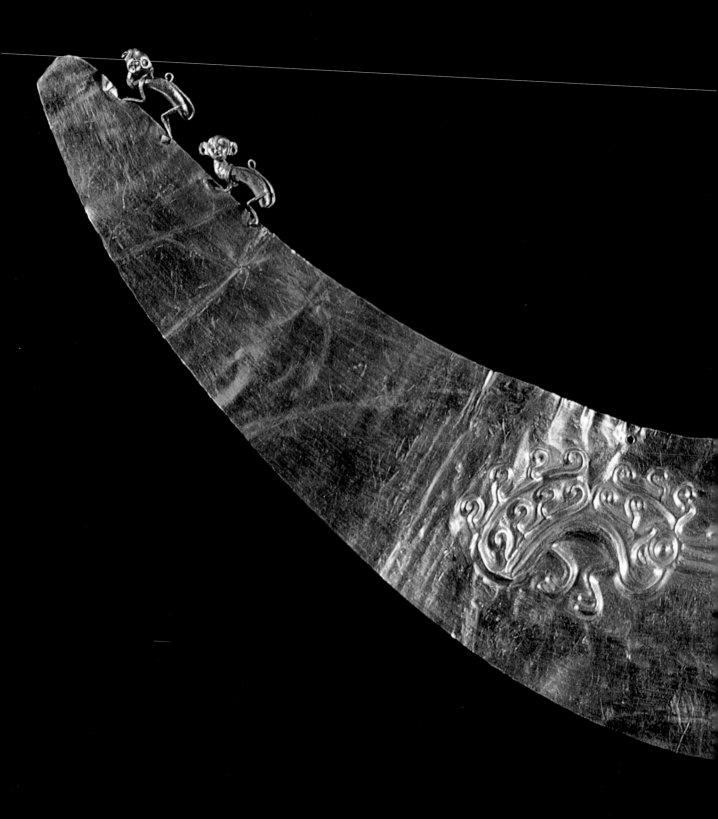

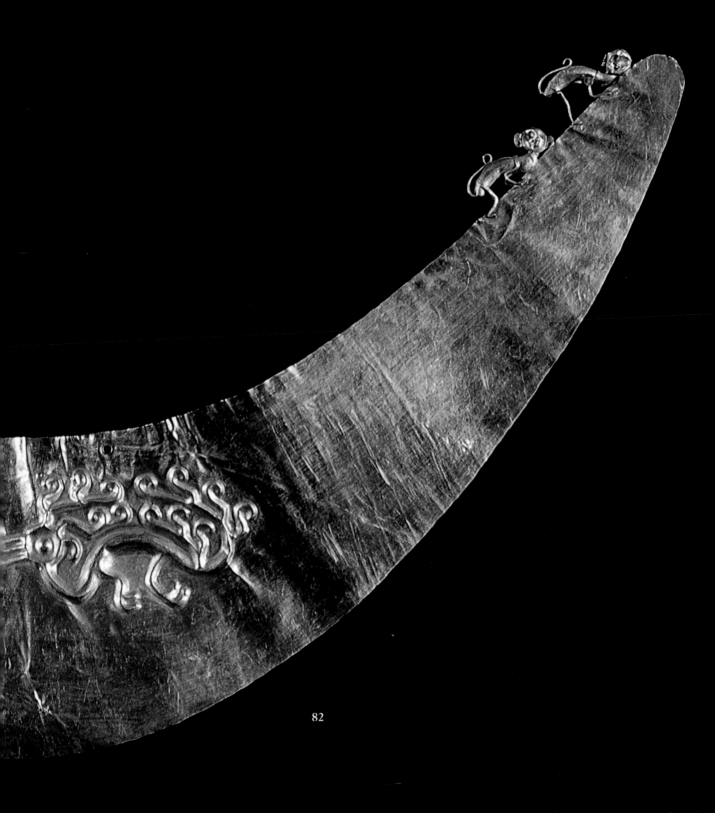

82

133

148

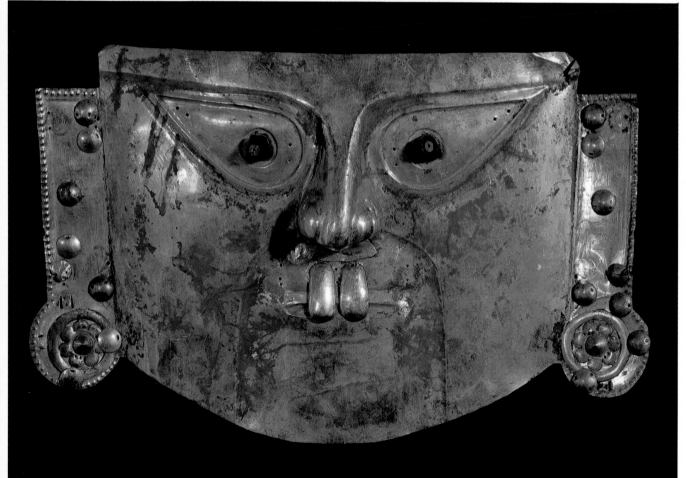

135

152

162

161

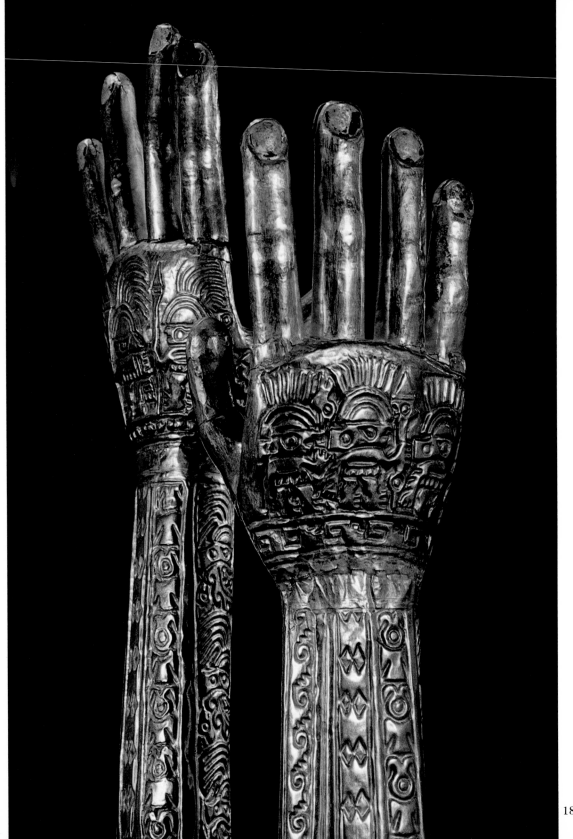

185, 186

205

221, 222

233

223

252

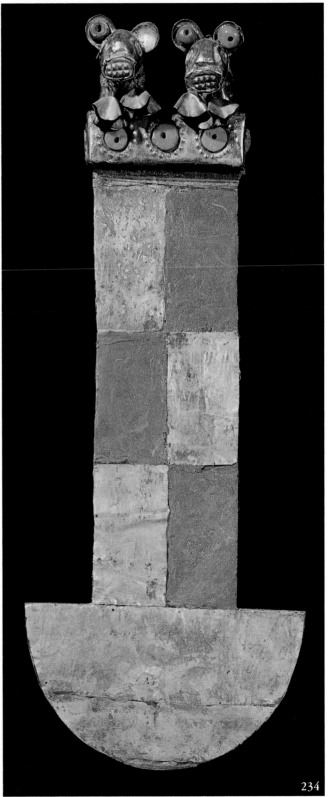

227

234

237

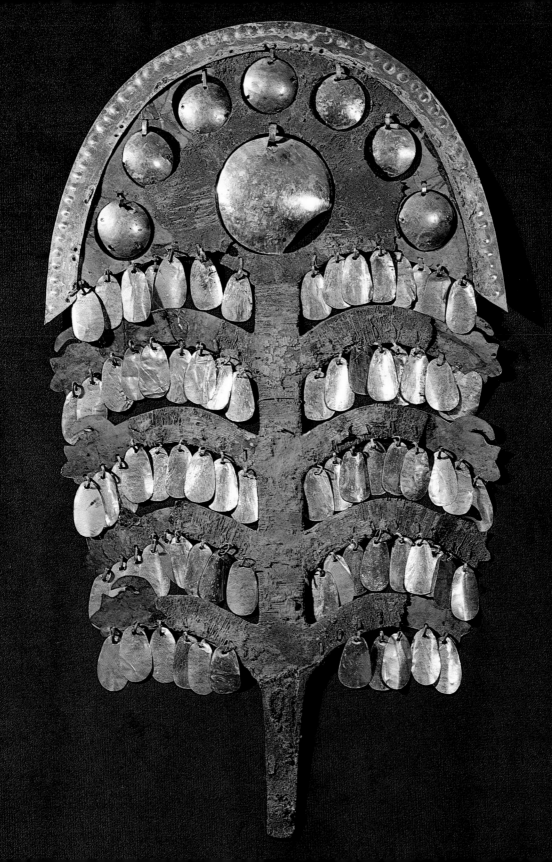

244

GOLD FOR THE GODS EXHIBITION
AND COMPLEMENTARY DISPLAYS

FLOOR PLAN – FIRST FLOOR

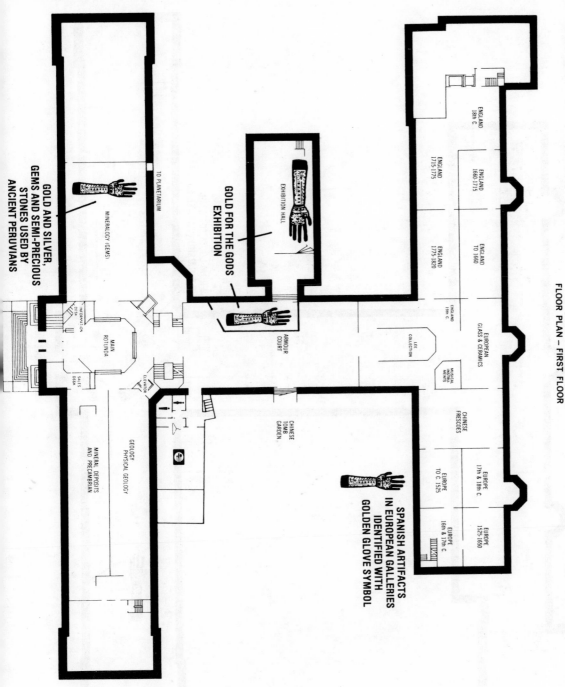

GOLD AND SILVER,
GEMS AND SEMI-PRECIOUS
STONES USED BY
ANCIENT PERUVIANS

GOLD FOR THE GODS
EXHIBITION

SPANISH ARTIFACTS
IN EUROPEAN GALLERIES
IDENTIFIED WITH
GOLDEN GLOVE SYMBOL

MINERALOGY (GEMS)

TO PLANETARIUM

EXHIBITION HALL

MAIN
ROTUNDA

INFORMATION
DESK

SALES
DESK

ELEVATOR

ARMOUR
COURT

CHINESE
TOMB
GARDEN

GEOLOGY
PHYSICAL GEOLOGY

MINERAL DEPOSITS
AND PRECAMBRIAN

ENGLAND
18th C.

ENGLAND
1660-1715

ENGLAND
1715-1775

ENGLAND
1775-1820

ENGLAND
TO 1660

ENGLAND
19th C.

EUROPEAN
GLASS & CERAMICS

LEE
COLLECTION

MUSICAL
INSTRU-
MENTS

CHINESE
FRESCOES

EUROPE
17th & 18th C.

EUROPE
TO C 1525

EUROPE
1525-1650

EUROPE
16th & 17th C.

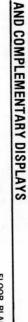

FLOOR PLAN – THIRD FLOOR

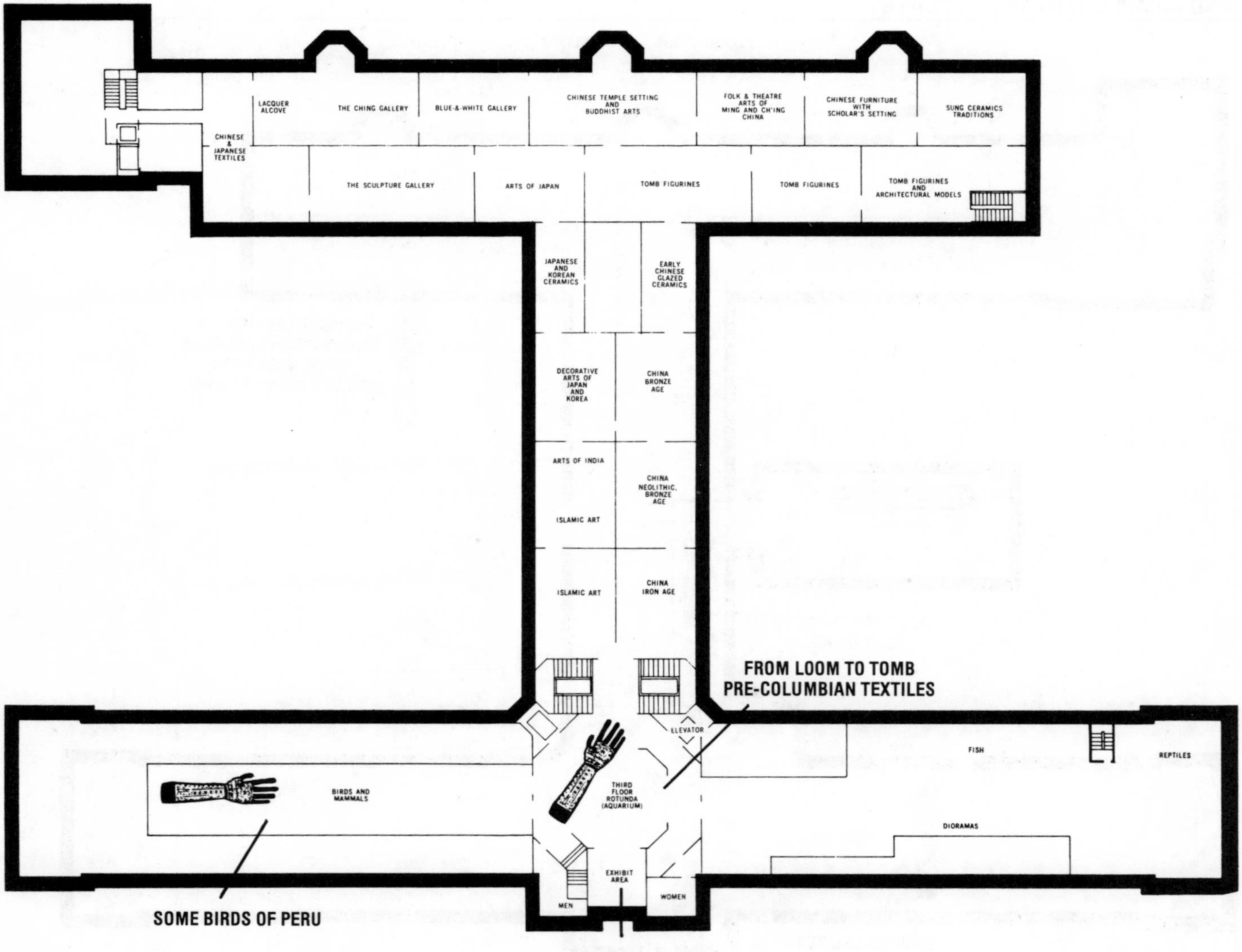

FROM LOOM TO TOMB
PRE-COLUMBIAN TEXTILES

SOME BIRDS OF PERU

INSECT DESIGN EXHIBIT

SUNG CERAMICS TRADITIONS

CHINESE FURNITURE WITH SCHOLAR'S SETTING

TOMB FIGURINES AND ARCHITECTURAL MODELS

FOLK & THEATRE ARTS OF MING AND CHING CHINA

TOMB FIGURINES

CHINESE TEMPLE SETTING AND BUDDHIST ARTS

TOMB FIGURINES

EARLY CHINESE GLAZED CERAMICS

CHINA BRONZE AGE

CHINA NEOLITHIC, BRONZE AGE

CHINA IRON AGE

BLUE & WHITE GALLERY

THE CHING GALLERY

LACQUER ALCOVE

CHINESE & JAPANESE TEXTILES

THE SCULPTURE GALLERY

ARTS OF JAPAN

JAPANESE AND KOREAN CERAMICS

DECORATIVE ARTS OF JAPAN AND KOREA

ARTS OF INDIA

ISLAMIC ART

ISLAMIC ART

ELEVATOR

THIRD FLOOR ROTUNDA (AQUARIUM)

EXHIBIT AREA

WOMEN

MEN

BIRDS AND MAMMALS

FISH

DIORAMAS

REPTILES

FLOOR PLAN – LOWER LEVEL

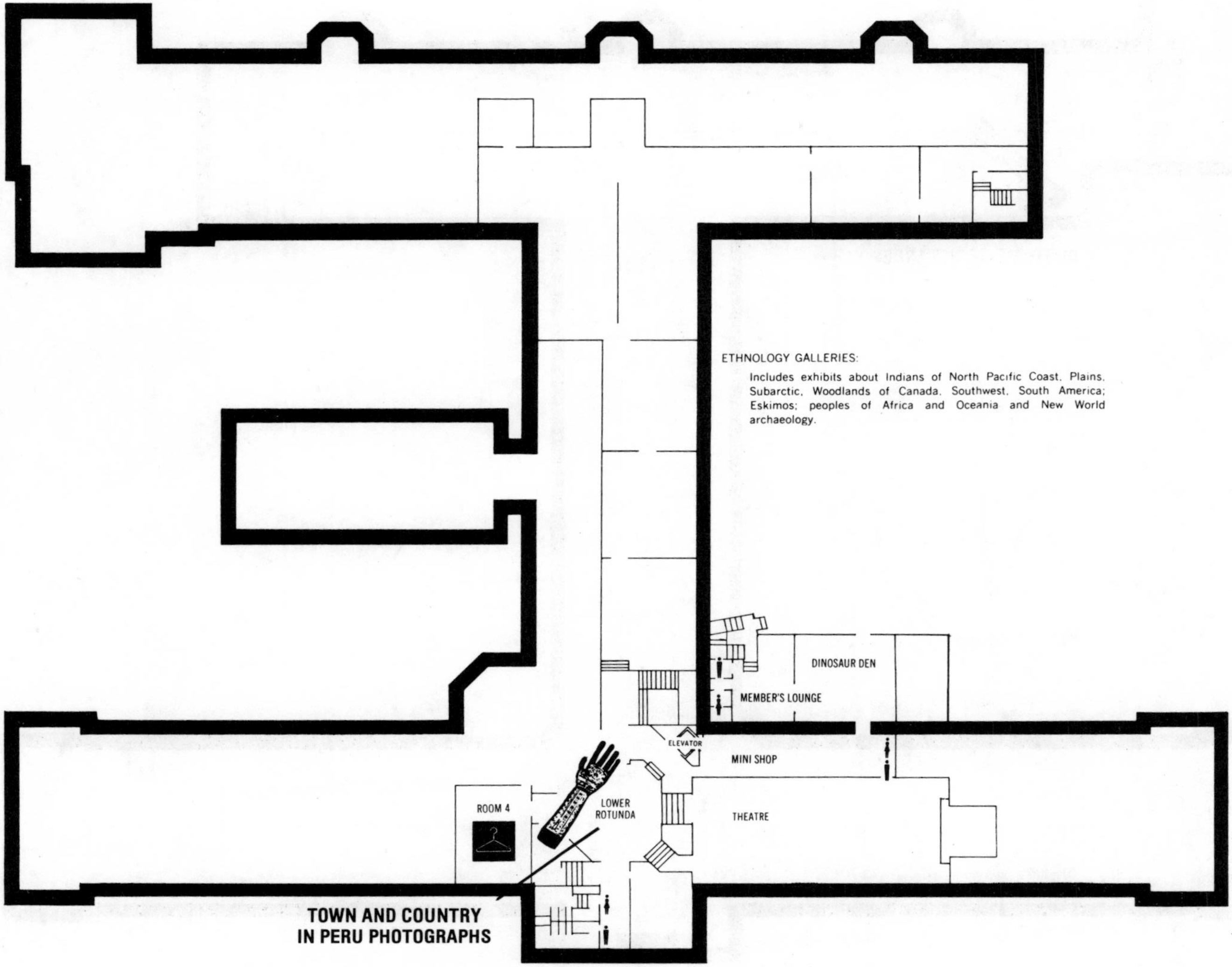

ETHNOLOGY GALLERIES:

Includes exhibits about Indians of North Pacific Coast, Plains, Subarctic, Woodlands of Canada, Southwest, South America; Eskimos; peoples of Africa and Oceania and New World archaeology.

DINOSAUR DEN

MEMBER'S LOUNGE

MINI SHOP

THEATRE

ELEVATOR

LOWER ROTUNDA

ROOM 4

TOWN AND COUNTRY IN PERU PHOTOGRAPHS

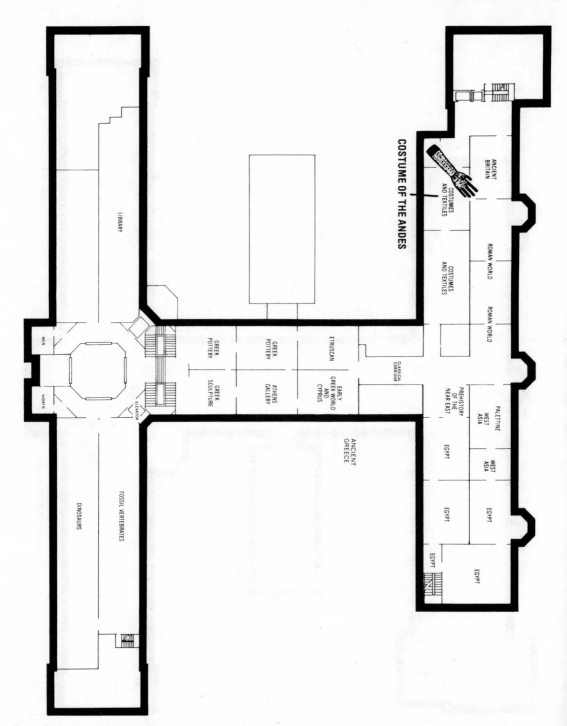

FLOOR PLAN – SECOND FLOOR

COSTUME OF THE ANDES

LIBRARY

MEN

WOMEN

ELEVATOR

GREEK POTTERY

GREEK POTTERY

GREEK SCULPTURE

ATHENS GALLERY

ETRUSCAN

EARLY GREEK WORLD AND CYPRUS

CLASSICAL CORRIDOR

ANCIENT GREECE

COSTUMES AND TEXTILES

COSTUMES AND TEXTILES

ANCIENT BRITAIN

ROMAN WORLD

ROMAN WORLD

PREHISTORY OF THE NEAR EAST

PALESTINE

WEST ASIA

WEST ASIA

EGYPT

EGYPT

EGYPT

EGYPT

EGYPT

DINOSAURS

FOSSIL VERTEBRATES

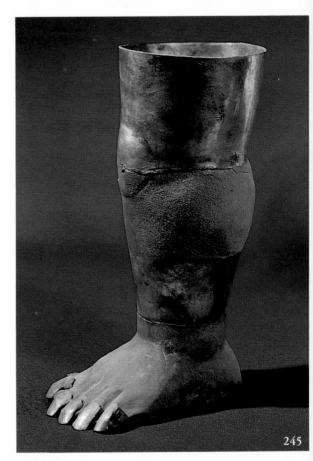

245

248, 249

226

271

254

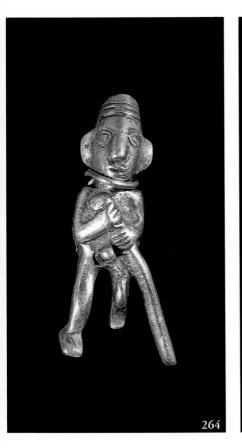

264

265

266

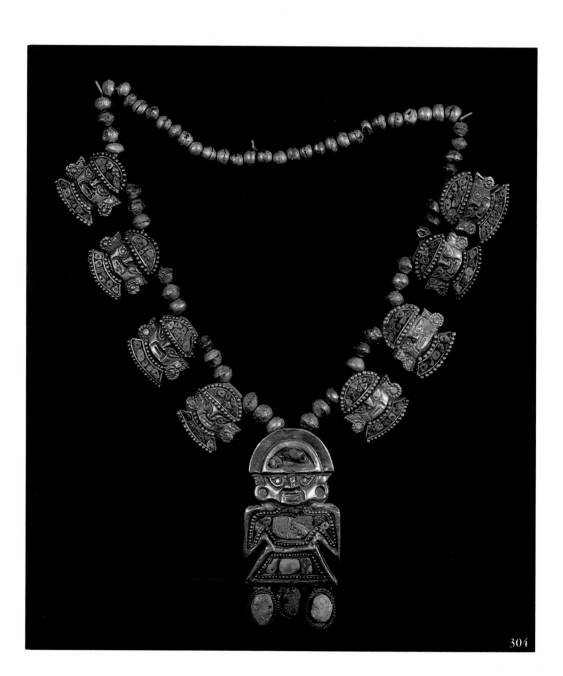

304

Catalogue Raisonné

Notes

1. Abbreviations

Each entry contains information in the following order: catalogue number, name of the object, description, provenance (if known), cultural affiliation (i.e., the culture period to which the object is ascribed), measurements, and, in square brackets, the registration number assigned by the Museo "Oro del Peru".

The following abbreviations are used:
L. — length
W. — width
H. — height
Th. — thickness
Diam. — diameter
✳denotes an object illustrated in the colour section.

2. Glossary of cultural terms

As all the objects come, as far as we know, from unscientific and clandestine excavations, the ascription of a provenance and a cultural affiliation must depend, ultimately, on the reliability of the diggers themselves and of the agents who acted on Señor Mujica's behalf. We can only be thankful that he was able to salvage and preserve for his country and the world so much of Peru's rich inheritance. We therefore accept the ascriptions and provenances given by Señor Mujica in his official guide to the collection (*Catalogue. Museum Gold of Peru* [Lima: Miguel Mujica Gallo Foundation, 1970]), except where some modification has been made on the basis of more recent discoveries or re-interpretations.

Dr. Day has discussed, in his essay on the archaeological history of Peru, the various stages through which Peruvian civilization passed, from the period of the hunter and gatherer to the fall of the Inca empire. We summarize here those periods and include sites listed in Señor Mújica's *Catalogue* to provide a key to the cultural affiliations and dates of the objects included in this exhibition. They are given in alphabetical order.

Chancay — a culture, characterized by black on white pottery, and particularly by large hollow figurines with this surface ornamentation, represented in the exhibition mainly by textiles and featherwork, but also by the remarkable funerary group (250). It had its centre in the region just north of modern Lima and was roughly contemporary with Chimu culture of the north coast, A.D. 1000-1470.

Chavin — the name given to an art style, the earliest of Peru's great styles, which spread over much of coastal Peru during the period 800-200 B.C. It takes its name from the site of Chavin de Huantar, where it was first recognized. The style manifested itself in distinctive ceremonial architecture, stone sculpture, and ceramics. Local varieties of the style are named Cupisnique, Sechin, and Paracas. Derivative elements, persistent in the Mochica and Nazca periods, are sometimes called "Chavinoid".

Chimu — a kingdom which, from its capital at Chan Chan in the Moche valley, controlled most of the northern coastal district of Peru. It lasted from about A.D. 1200 to 1470. The bulk of the gold objects in the exhibition date from this period.

Cupisnique — the name applied to a style of ceramics found in cemeteries of the Chicama valley in northern Peru which have produced material of the Chavin period.

Frias — a town in the extreme north of Peru, whose cemeteries have produced quantities of gold assigned now to the Mochica period, about A.D. 200-400.

Huari— a site in the southern highlands of Peru, occupied between about A.D. 600 and 900. Huari style ceramics have been found on the south coast of Peru following the Nazca period (see Tiahuanaco).

Inca — the kingdom, with its capital at Cuzco in the mountains southeast of Lima, which expanded rapidly from about the middle of the 15th century A.D. to create an empire which included Peru, parts of Ecuador and Chile, Bolivia, and Argentina. It fell to the Spaniards under Pizarro in A.D. 1532.

Lambayeque — the name of a valley in northern Peru. In this valley, the ruined site of Batan Grande, of the Mochica/Chimu period, appears to be the source of much of the gold in the Mujica collection. From this site, probably, come those pieces with representations of the human face characterized by a sharply upturning outer corner of the eye, which is known as the "Lambayeque eye" and which is typical of the "Lambayeque style". Pampa Grande, another site in the same valley, appears to precede the Chimu kingdom, but to be closely linked to it and to the earlier Mochica culture. Together, Batan Grande and Pampa Grande may span the gap between the last stages of the Mochica culture and the triumph of the Chimu nation.

Lauri — a cemetery site of the Chancay culture.

Mochica — the dominant culture on the north coast of Peru from about A.D. 200 to about 800-900, taking its name from an important ceremonial centre in the Moche river valley. The Mochica built massive truncated pyramids in many of the valleys on the north coast and produced great quantities of fine ceramics. The Vicus culture is here considered to represent a proto-Mochica and early Mochica phase. The Salinar culture is probably also proto-Mochica, but the Frias culture is probably contemporary with early Mochica.

Nazca — the culture that flourished on the south coast of Peru roughly contemporaneously with the Mochica in the north, from about the beginning of the Christian era to A.D. 600. Distinctive ceramics and magnificent textiles were found at the site named "Paracas Necropolis". It is apparently to this period also that the great "earth drawings" belong, which were created on the ground by the removal of surface stones, and which represent animals, birds, arrows, spirals, and straight lines.

Paracas — a peninsula on the south coast of Peru famous for its hundreds of burials which have preserved large quantities of magnificent textiles in almost every possible form of weaving, embroidery, and colouring. The "Paracas Cavernas" may be of the Chavin period, but the "Paracas Necropolis" dates to the early part of the Nazca period, about the beginning of the Christian era.

Salinar — a large cemetery in the upper Chicama valley in northern Peru, with pottery influenced by Chavin styles and probably preceding Mochica.

Sechin — a site in the Casma valley west of Chavin de Huantar with architectural sculpture of the Chavin period or slightly earlier.

Tiahuanaco — a site at the south end of Lake Titicaca in Bolivia. The art style expressed in carved stone monuments and ceramics at this site appears in a different guise at the site of Huari in the southern highlands of Peru about A.D. 600-800.

Vicus — a village in the extreme north of Peru, whose tombs have produced distinctive gold objects such as nose pendants with surfaces partly of gold, partly of silver. It is considered a subculture of the Mochica period and is dated roughly 200 B.C.-A.D. 300.

3. Metals and metallurgy

The use of the terms "gold" and "silver" in the catalogue also requires some explanation. The essay on metallurgy demonstrates that, in fact, we are dealing with alloys — usually, if not always, artificial — which have served as the base from which a silver surface, a gold surface, or a mixed silver and gold surface was produced by a process of hammering, annealing, and pickling. The thickness of the surface layer depended on the amounts of the constituent metals in the basic alloy and on the number of times the hammered sheet was subjected to annealing and pickling. At times, it was so thin that it could actually be worn off or, if the other metals broke through and became corroded, covered over with corrosion products — oxides, carbonates, etc. It is not always easy, therefore, to decide what the original surface was. In most cases, we have assumed that a yellow colour denotes an original gold surface and a white colour an original silver surface. There are a few cases where we must recognize the possibility that platinum is present, but in the absence of metallurgical analysis we can say nothing more.

4. Jewellery

We are in somewhat the same position when it comes to the problem of the semi-precious stones used in jewellery or inset into some of the objects. There is true turquoise in Peru, but another stone, chrysocolla, which has much the same appearance, is also used. When the former term is used, it must be taken in a very general way to include both stones; where the latter is used, there is some evidence (usually from the registration forms prepared by Peru's Instituto Nacional de Cultura) that an analysis has been made. The fact is, however, that while all the stones named are found in Peru or could have been traded in from surrounding countries, our identifications are normally based on appearance, not analysis.

5. Functional terminology

In some cases we have used terms, such as "tweezers", *tumi,* and "crowns", that have become traditional. The "tweezers" (in Spanish *depiladores*) *may* have had their origin in utensils for plucking out hair, but seem to have become more generally a form of ornament used in necklaces and other objects. Such a development is understandable when one remembers that in pre-Inca times, most, if not all, products in gold and silver were worked up from sheet metal. This fact limited greatly the shapes and types of objects that could be produced. Tiny embossed gold hemispheres or ovoid forms could be soldered together to make hollow beads; cut-out shapes, embossed or plain, could be sewn on garments; beakers, bowls, and jars could be created by "raising". Complex forms, such as the rattle (116), became possible with the exercise of some ingenuity. But because the field of opportunity was so limited, the use for ornamental purposes of a form which had been developed for purely utilitarian purposes could be expected. Whether or not this is the true development, there is little doubt that the "tweezers", in fact, are frequently purely decorative.

The word *tumi* has been retained because it designates a very distinctive form for which there is no easy English substitute. The term "crown" is somewhat more difficult to define. It is an ornamental headdress, of course, but it is not easy to distinguish between a cap or hat which is somewhat more ornate than usual, on the one hand, and a ceremonial object on the other; or, for that matter, between a military helmet with a lofty crest and a civilian or hieratic crown. We have simply avoided a sharp distinction by using the term to describe a non-military headdress which was probably worn on special occasions by a person of rank, whether he was the divine king himself or a lesser official.

1-4. Gold nuggets, an ingot, and partially hammered ingot, showing various stages of smelting and working process.
[4157, 4159, 4165, 4167].✱

5, 6. Two of about 25 or 30 round plates of metal with two or three square punchholes for suspension by cords. Gold, silver, and copper are all present. Traces of textile adhere to surface. Vicus.
Diams. from about 35 to 45 cm;
Th. 0.3-0.4 cm
[4011, 4012]

7-18. Twelve stones in shades from light grey through brown to black and of very fine grain, shaped and polished for use in forming and burnishing metal.
L. of pestle 9.5 cm; L. of smallest stone, pointed at both ends, 5.5 cm
[1611, 1612, 1625, 1627, 1633, 1661, 1687, 1695, 1697, 1706, 1730, 1745]

19. Crouching jaguar. One of seven known, almost identical, figures discovered in 1924 at Pampa Grande, 17 km southwest of Chongoyape, in the Lambayeque valley in northern Peru. Each is formed of 12 individual pieces, cut out and embossed, and welded and soldered together. The skin markings are grooved in intaglio. Two specimens contain a pebble, indicating that they were intended to rattle. The small perforations on the underside suggest they were originally sewn to a head-band, shirt, or belt, or formed part of a necklace. The average of tests made on one specimen, apparently valid for all, indicates a composition of 8.9% copper, 14.9% silver, and 75.9% gold. Chavinoid style, probably early Mochica. For further details see Heather Lechtman, Lee A. Parsons, and William J. Young, *Seven Matched Hollow Gold Jaguars from Peru's Early Horizon,* Studies in Pre-Columbian Art & Archaeology, no. 16 (Washington, D.C.: Dumbarton Oaks, Trustees for Harvard University, 1975).
L. 10.3 cm
[2514]✱

20, 21. Two rectangular shell plaques (from ear spools?) inlaid with turquoise in the form of stylized human faces. Proto-Mochica. Salinar.
H. 6.5 cm; W. 5 cm
[1144, 1145]

22. Nose ornament of gold with embossed human face in silver. Vicus.
H. 4.7 cm; W. 4.7 cm
[3626]

23. Nose ornament in gold; two facing birds (?) with crests and long, monkey-like tails. Vicus.
H. 7.6 cm; W. 4.9 cm
[3629]

24. Nose ornament in rectangular form divided diagonally into two zones of gold of different colour. Vicus.
H. 3.9 cm; W. 5.4 cm
[3680]

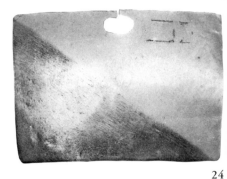

24

20, 21

25. Nose ornament of gold ornamented with very stylized zoomorphic motifs. Vicus.
H. 7 cm; W. 10.4 cm
[3570]

26. Nose ornament in gold ornamented with a central anthropomorphic mask from which project symmetrically curved lines and two birds (?). Vicus.
H. 7.2 cm; W. 9.4 cm
[3575]

27. Nose ornament in gold; two facing birds(?) with crests and long monkey-like tails. Vicus.
H. 8.6 cm; W. 12 cm
[3564]

28. Nose ornament with eight rows of embossed circles with central point. Vicus.
H. 8.8 cm; W. 12 cm
[3565]

29. Nose ornament with highly stylized anthromorphic mask. Vicus.
H. 7.8 cm; W. 11.2 cm
[3568]

30. Nose ornament with two rows of crested birds(?), like 27. Vicus.
H. 8.1 cm; W. 11.2 cm
[3567]

31. Nose ornament with anthropomorphic(?) mask bordered by a double-headed serpent (?). Vicus.
H. 6.3 cm; W. 7.4 cm
[3436]

32. Nose ornament consisting of irregular bands of silver and gold bearing an anthropomorphic mask. Vicus.
H. 8.1 cm; W. 10.5 cm
[3365]

27

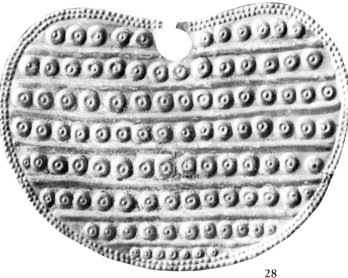

28

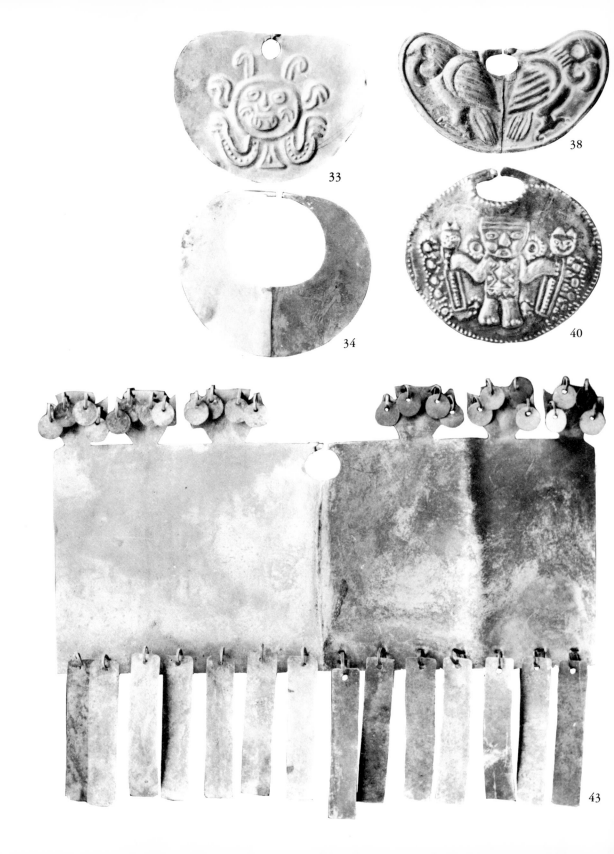

33

38

34

40

43

33. Nose ornament of gold with an anthropomorphic face from which curved lines radiate. Vicus.
H. 7 cm; W. 9.4 cm
[3367]

34. Nose ornament, half gold, half silver. Vicus.
H. 7.7 cm; W. 9.4 cm
[3327]

35. Nose ornament with four monkeys (?). Vicus.
H. 5.7 cm; W. 9.4 cm
[3558]

36. Nose ornament with a central anthropomorphic figure holding two clubs (?) standing on a two-headed beast. Vicus.
H. 5.5 cm; W. 7.3 cm
[3560]

37. Nose ornament, half gold, half silver, representing a stylized human face (?), whose eyes represent small faces. Vicus.
H. 12.8 cm; W. 16.3 cm
[3364]

38. Nose ornament, gold and silver, with bird figures. Vicus.
H. 3.8 cm; W. 7.7 cm
[3687]

39. Nose ornament of plain gold. Vicus.
H. 6 cm; W. 7.6 cm
[3586]

40. Nose ornament of gold depicting an anthropomorphic figure with ear ornaments, bearing two staffs which have feline (?) finials. Vicus.
H. 6.4 cm; W. 7.4 cm
[3351]

41. Nose ornament of gold with simple embossed decoration. Vicus.
H. 5 cm; W. 6.5 cm
[3421]

42. Nose ornament of silver and gold in V-shape; at the base a human head in relief with pendant spangles and flanked by squirrels. Vicus.
H. 11 cm; W. 17 cm
[3361]*

43. Rectangular nose ornament. Half silver (?), half gold, with pendant decorations at top and bottom. Vicus.
H. 16.7 cm; W. 21.8 cm
[3556]

44. Large gold nose ornament of semi-elliptical shape. Completely plain with traces of red and black paint (?) Vicus.
Greatest W. 28.6 cm
[2507]

45. Nose ornament of gold and silver. Vicus.
H. 5.7 cm; W. 7.8 cm
[3362]

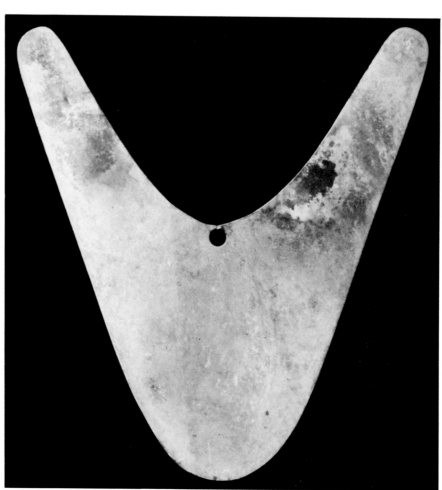

44

46. Alligator in embossed gold with tubular pendants below. Vicus.
L. 8 cm
[341]

47. Ornament of lapis lazuli in semi-circular form with border of gold cut wire and spherical beads. Vicus.
H. 2.5 cm; W. 3.8 cm
[2352]

48-50. Thimbles, bobbins, or finials of cylindrical form with conical and spherical protrusions on top. One is ornamented with turquoise and shell. Vicus.
Hs. 2.5 cm, 2 cm, 1.7 cm
[5275, 5276, 5282]

51. Bowl of hemispherical form converging towards a plain rim and with a convex base. The embossed decoration consists of four stylized human faces with prominent eyebrows, round eyes, and rectangular mouths, alternating with panels of semicircles and tiny bosses. Traces of red paint. Vicus.
H. 8 cm; Diam. of rim 13.5 cm
[4679]

52. Gold bowl, globular in form with in-turning rim. Lower part of body embossed with panels containing a stylized human head *en face* flanked by monkey (?) heads in profile, separated by panels containing rows of backward S-forms. Vicus.
H. 6.3 cm; Diam. of rim 8.6 cm
[4674]

53. Silver funerary mask with gold ear ornaments, inlaid with turquoise beads and bearing representations of squirrels. Iron oxide (?) running down from one eye. Vicus?
H. 18 cm; W. 28.5 cm
[1226]∗

54. Anthropomorphic mask in embossed gold with eyes, ears, and mouth inset with carved shell. Vicus.
H. 9.8 cm; W. 10.5 cm
[2213]

51

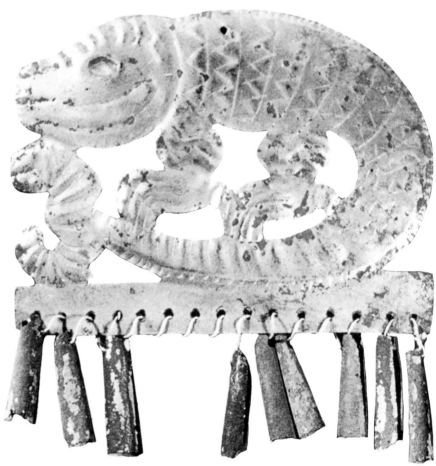

46

96

55. Feline head in embossed gold with carved shell eyes and teeth. Gold, painted red and perhaps originally also decorated with feathers. Vicus.
H. 8 cm; W. 10.7 cm
[2216]

56. "Tweezer" pendant. Stylized human head upon a crescent-shaped, two-headed serpent. A pair of undulating, two-headed serpents rises from the head representing, perhaps, the hair. Wires are threaded through the ears of the human head. A horizontal tubular form at the top served for suspension. Vicus.
H. 5.1 cm; W. 7.3 cm
[2675]

57. Mask. Gold sheet with holes for eyes and mouth, and nose cut out on three sides only. Almost completely covered with small circular discs secured by wire staples (83 remaining). Vicus.
H. 18.5 cm; W. 19 cm
[3772]✷

58. Small mask in gold with heavy copper corrosion, embossed in high relief. The representation of a cloth band passes across the forehead, down the sides of the face, and below the chin. A headdress of cylindrical form bears four rows of discs (of which three discs remain) attached by wire. Eyes are inlaid with white shell, which, in turn, has pinkish shell inlays for pupils. Vicus.
H. 14 cm; W. 10 cm
[3861)]✷

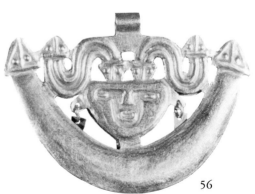

54

55

56

59. Spider. One of many in the Museo Oro del Peru collection with body embossed in two parts and folded together. Legs and antennae of wire. Gold with much copper oxide encrustation. Vicus.
L. of body 4 cm
[3889]

60. Round plaque, much worn so that gold has rubbed off leaving silver surface. Decoration of incised whorl design and random squares. Vicus.
Diam. 8.5 cm
[3834]

61. Small mask embossed in high relief. Humanoid face with square eyes inlaid with gold (?); mouth covered with gold and provided with shell fangs. A gold disc pendant hangs from the nose. Surface is badly corroded. Vicus?
L. 8 cm; greatest W. 7.8 cm
[22]

62. Ornament, possibly a pectoral. Rectangular lattice consisting of six horizontal and nine vertical strips; from the points of intersection hang pendants in the form of *tumi* blades (49) and cones (5). Mochica (Frias).
H. 16.2 cm; W. 27.1 cm
[2442]

63. "Tweezer" pendant. Fragment (?) of a zoomorphic figure with wire mouth, teeth, and spirals as a mane or crest. A turquoise bead marks the eye. Mochica (Frias).
H. 3.4 cm; W. 4.2 cm
[2513]

64. Ear spool. The border of the roundel is a rope pattern in wire, soldered to the disc edge. The disc has radiating lines of triangles and, at the centre, the muzzle of a fanged animal in high relief. Looped wires securing discs and other pendants protrude from the roundel and the animal head. Mochica (Frias).
Diam. 7.7 cm
[1951]

65. Bracelet. A series of square gold plaques with applied filigree volutes bordered on both sides by tiny gold balls. Mochica (Frias?).
L. 18.3 cm
[881]

66. Bracelet. Four strands of square gold plaques with applied filigree volutes, each strand terminating, at both ends, in a clasp formed from a central turquoise bead surrounded by tiny gold balls. Restrung? Mochica (Frias?).
L. 20.3 cm
[884]

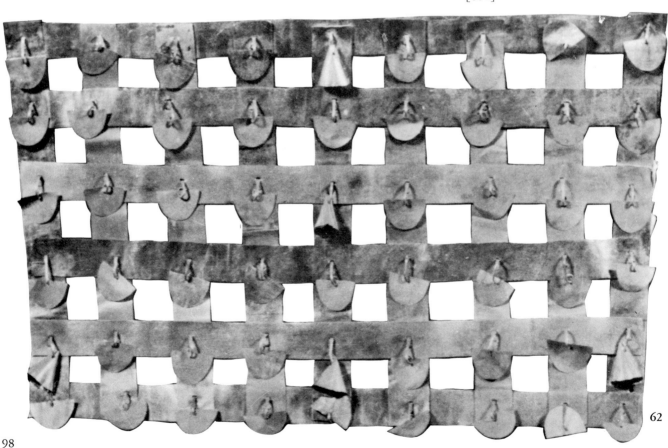

62

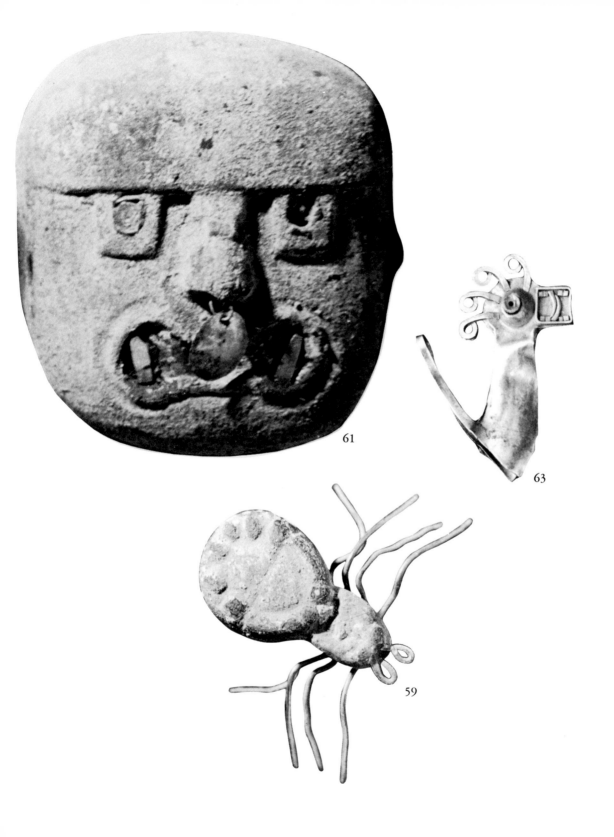

61

63

59

67. Gold needle. Mochica (Frias).
L. 8.3 cm
[2407]

68. Gold needle. Mochica (Frias).
L. 7.6 cm
[2408]

69-72. Four gold spatulas and gravers.
Mochica (Frias).
69. L. 12.7 cm; greatest W. 3.8 cm
[2411]
70. L. 10.5 cm; greatest W. 0.4 cm
[2412]
71. L. 11 cm; greatest W. 2.3 cm
[2413]
72. L. 6.8 cm; greatest W. 0.6 cm
[2414]

73. Diadem. A plain band of gold supports;
at its lower edge, seven birds in the round
(one now lacking its head) with turquoise
bead eyes and gold spangles; the central
bird is larger than the others. On the basis
of the remaining gold staples, there were
originally four more birds. The embossed
plume may not originally have formed
part of the ensemble. Mochica (Frias).
H. (with plume) 18 cm; W. of band 5 cm
[2900]

74. Bag of rectangular shape made of
tapestry-woven striped material bordered
at the top with a "knitted" band, and
provided with a ribbon strap in repp.
Against the body fabric of black, ochre,
and white are sewn (on both sides) two
gold-foil monkeys, back to back, holding
a head (?) and a circular object in each
hand. The remainder of the field, on one
side, contains geometric forms including
wave patterns, double-headed snakes, etc.;
on the other, the lower edge has a row of
monkeys. Mochica (Frias).
H. (without strap) 24 cm; W. 34 cm;
L. of strap 55 cm
[4132]*

75, 76. Pair of pendants of gold and rock
crystal, each with three triangular pendants.
Mochica (Frias).
H. 3 cm; W. 1.7 cm
[2349, 2350]

77. Ornamental bird. Hammered and embossed in the round in sections to which
are attached separate sheets for wings and
tail. Supported on a circular base of cut-
wire work. Mochica (Frias).
H. 4.2 cm
[2694]

78, 79. Pair of "tweezer" pendants in circular form representing two intertwined
serpents. Mochica (Frias).
Diam. 4 cm
[2677, 2683]

80. Small spoon in shape of serpent with
triangular head. Mochica (Frias).
L. 18.5 cm
[4548]

81. Small spoon with flat handle terminating in cut-wire spirals. Mochica (Frias).
L. 8.2 cm
[4551]

82. Pectoral in the form of a new moon
with two fanciful birds in the middle and
two monkeys in the round fastened to the
upper edge at both ends. Mochica (Frias).
L. 46.5 cm
[2716]*

83, 84. Pair of pendants of zoomorphic
form with wire spirals for horns and tails.
The eyes consist of turquoise beads surrounded with wire, and similar beads
adorn the bodies. From the mouths and
lower parts of the bodies and tails hang
triangular pendants. Mochica (Frias).
H. of each, 4.5 cm
[2705, 2706]

85, 86. Pair of pendants. A ring supports
a humming-bird (?) with eyes of turquoise
beads (missing in one). Mochica (Frias).
H. 8 cm each; W. 5.5, 5.7 cm
[2489, 2490]

87, 88. Pair of pendants with bird bodies
and human faces, one retaining 10 small
triangular pendants. Mochica (Frias).
H. 3.2 cm; W. 4 cm
[2520, 2521]

89. "Tweezer" pendant. Stylized head of
a parrot (?) with embossed features.
Mochica (Frias).
H. 3.4 cm; W. 3.3 cm
[2687]

90. Pendant composed of a two-headed
feline and a bird. Facial features are outlined in wire. Pendants of various geometric shapes held by wires form crests on
the feline heads and hang from the bird.
Turquoise beads are inserted into the eyes.
Mochica (Frias).
H. 6 cm; W. 4.5 cm
[2531]

91. Pendant. A large ring supports a long-
beaked bird with turquoise bead eyes. Nine
tumi blade-shaped pendants are suspended
by wire loops from the body, and an embossed pendant from the beak. Mochica
(Frias).
L. 5 cm; Diam. of ring 3.3 cm
[2497]

69-72

73

77

87, 88

91

89

92

94

95

92, 93. Pair of pedestal cups with rounded bowl and flaring base. Mochica (Frias).
   92. H. 10.5 cm; Diam of rim 12.7 cm
   93. H. 9.4 cm; Diam. of rim 12.8 cm
[4554, 4555]

94. Hemispherical gold bowl with convex base, decorated with two rows of gold spangles secured by gold wire. Mochica (Frias).
H. 7 cm; Diam. of rim 10.5 cm
[4546]

95. Hemispherical gold bowl with convex base. Mochica (Frias).
H. 6.7 cm; Diam. of rim 13.5 cm
[4561]

96. Pin with a stylized bird mounted on the back of a monkey as a finial. Many details worked in gold wire. Turquoise beads form the bird's eyes. Mochica (Frias).
H. 15.6 cm
[2508]

97. Lizard with separately made head and legs. Ornamental discs are attached by wires to the chest and stomach. Mochica (Frias).
L. 19.7 cm
[2691]✶

98. Plume. A stylized feather with flaring sides made of hammered gold attached to a quill or support. Mochica (Frias).
L. 42.6 cm
[2509]

99. Puma. A stylized feline with body, legs, and tail of hammered sheet gold embossed with a pattern of double-headed serpents. The head is embossed in high relief with attached tongue, teeth, and ears. Mochica (Frias).
L. 64 cm
[3051]✶

100. Small stylized anthropoid figure, clothed in an enveloping poncho or mantle from which the hands and feet project, seated on a serpent's head. The distinctive headdress, the human features, and the lineaments of the serpent's head are carefully emphasized in wire, plain and rope pattern. Mochica (Frias).
H. 8.6 cm
[2344]

101. "Tweezer" pendant. A gold ring supports "tweezers" in lunate form, ornamented at the ends with complex, stylized feline heads and, on top, with a monkey. Mochica (Frias).
H. 10.8 cm; W. 11.5 cm
[2328]

102. "Tweezer" pendant. A gold loop supports "tweezers" in the form of a double-headed serpent. Mochica (Frias).
H. 4.4 cm; W. 7.6 cm
[2689]

103. "Tweezer" pendant in the form of a gold crescent with a silver loop. Mochica (Frias).
H. 4 cm; W. 6.2 cm
[2679]

104. Ear spool. The muzzle of a fanged animal decorated with suspended discs protrudes in high relief from the centre of the disc, and a serpent coils around the edge. The remainder of the decoration consists of hemispherical beads and pendant discs. The spool behind the roundel is a tube of sheet gold. Mochica.
Diam. 8 cm
[1952]

105, 106. Matched pair of gold ear spools mounted on silver tubes. Embossed warrior figures with inset turquoise beads. No. 106 retains some traces of matt pinkish paint background. Mochica.
Diam. 7.5 cm
[4922, 4923]

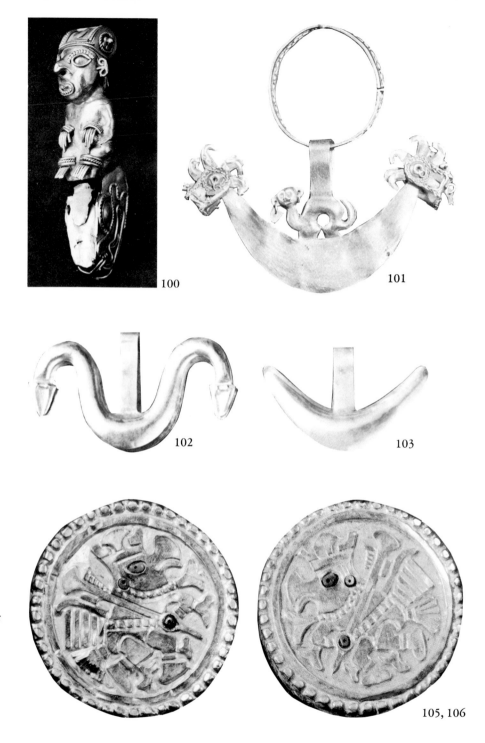

100

101

102

103

105, 106

107, 108. Pair of finials embossed with human faces and topped with a hollow ball. Mochica?
H. 4.9 cm
[2829, 2830]

109. Rectangular stone plaque with incised scene. Two "warriors" are represented as walking or running towards one another. They wear skirts and broad belts from which a plume (?) streams out behind. Each carries a long staff with a heavy head; each has a red *Spondylus*-bead eye and a turquoise-bead ear ornament. The right-hand figure is looking to the left and appears to have seized the wrist of the other, who has turned his head away, also to the left. Five holes are bored around the perimeter of the plaque (which is of a very fine grey stone) for securing it to some backing. Mochica.
L. 10.7 cm; greatest W. 7.9 cm; Th. 0.35 cm
[2852]

110-113. Four bird finials of embossed gold with cut wire for crests and beaks; usually with turquoise beads for eyes. Mochica?
Hs. 3.7-3.9 cm
[Unnumbered]

114. Small anthropomorphic mask embossed in high relief; a cloth (?) headdress passes across the forehead and hangs down on either side of the face. Remains of the tube for an ear ornament remain in one ear. Eyes originally inlaid with white shell in which a pupil of red *Spondylus* shell is set (only one eye retains the inlay). Red paint adheres to the gold in several places. Mochica?
L. 8.1 cm; greatest W. 7.8 cm
[3]

115. Small mask embossed in high relief with cloth headdress coming low on the forehead. The eyes are inlaid with shell and have holes for insertion of the pupils (presumably like 114), but these now missing. Probably originally covered with red and blue paint. Mochica?
H. 5.5 cm; greatest W. 4.9 cm; Depth (with nose) 2.9 cm
[317]✷

116. Rattle. A single sheet of gold is embossed and bent to form a flat axe-head shape with a flaring crescent blade and a cluster of six gourd forms. A horizontal tube between the gourd forms presumably allows the whole to swivel on a handle. Traces of red paint still adhere. Mochica?
L. 32.6 cm; W. (across axe-head) 23.8 cm
[265]

109

114

116

117

117, 118. Pair of ear ornaments. A disc with a trapezoidal pendant supporting strips in serpentine form with triangular heads. Profusely decorated, with applied small discs and semicircular spangles. In the centre of the disc there is a bird with inlaid turquoise eyes. Mochica.
   117 L. 28.8 cm; Diam. of disc 10.4 cm
   118 L. 28.5 cm; Diam. of disc 10.6 cm
   [1900, 1901]

119. Bird-shaped nose cover (?). Paracas.
L. 12.5 cm; W. 26.6 cm
[2250]

120. Bird-shaped nose cover (?). Paracas.
L. 10.6 cm; W. 27.1 cm
[2253]

121, 122. Pair of stylized bats. Traces of red paint. Nazca.
   121 H. 26.8 cm; W. 31 cm
   122 H. 26.5 cm; W. 31 cm
   [2248, 2244]

123. Mouth mask. On each side project four "whiskers" in serpent form; curving upward and inward are four other elements, two in serpent, two in bird (?) form. The lower part, which covered the mouth, is circular with a dentate border. Nazca.
H. 23.8 cm; W. 21 cm
[3236]

124. Mouth mask. The lower part, which encircled the mouth, consists of an embossed disc with a serrated outer edge and an off-centre central hole. The upper part is formed of five embossed serpent bodies and heads. Nazca.
H. 13 cm; W. 15 cm
[2222]

125. Gold ear cleaner (?) with cast parrot finial. Nazca.
L. 6.7 cm
[2305]

126. Silver ear cleaner (?) with hummingbird finial. Nazca.
L. 8 cm
[4823]

122

123

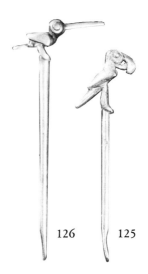

126   125

127. Feather headdress. A textile of tapestry weave, formed into a tube and supported vertically by eight flat wooden sticks, supports two tiers of large vertical feathers and, below, a narrow border of two rows of small feathers running horizontally. In front is a thin rectangular gold plaque embossed with a stylized mask and plume. To one side is a tassel of red wool suspended from a woven, tubular, seamless, three-dimensional cord. Nazca.
Overall H. 34 cm
[3702]

127

128

128. Feather headdress. A broad tapestry-woven band in red, blue, and green, with stylized human figures, birds, serpents, and other patterns, above which a cotton string (now covered with white wool) supports a series of gold pendants; above this border white (and two brown) feathers rise vertically. Nazca.
Overall H. 26 cm
[3714]

129

129. Doll. The body consists of a reed armature roughly modelled. There are two skirts, the outer of cotton decorated with 11 zigzag-shaped gold-foil plaques; the underskirt, also of cotton, with inserted tapestry-woven strip in a geometrical pattern. The waist is wrapped twice around with a repp cotton band. The shirt is of red and yellow-greenish material, and into it are stuck two disc-headed shawl pins. The facial features are embroidered; the hair is of loose woollen threads. The hands are wound about with wool; on the right hand, which holds a spindle, are rings and a bracelet, while another spindle is stuck in above the waist. There are eight strands of beads around the neck and a strand around the forehead. Nazca.
H. 38 cm
[3762]

130. "Wrist guard" (?) decorated with rows of bosses, circles, and zigzag lines. Nazca.
L. 7.3 cm
[3264]

131. "Wrist guard" embossed with eight vertical rows of quatrefoil bosses. Nazca.
L. 19.9 cm
[3238]

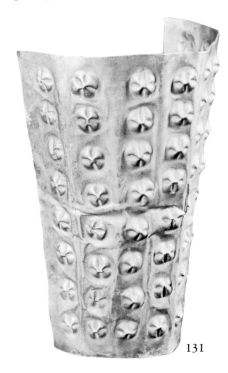

131

132. Sash. Tapestry-woven band with dull red bordering a brown-on-yellow geometric pattern. At the ends, thick disc-shaped ornaments in red textile bear human features in black-and-white and terminate in long red-and-black fringes. Highly embossed, oval gold ornaments adorn the belt and surround the faces. Nazca.
L. (with fringes) 183 cm; W. 6.5 cm
[4153]

133. One of a pair of high-domed caps or helmets formed of reeds bent and sewn together with heavy cord and covered with gold foil in short tubular sections. Nazca.
H. 19 cm; Diam. 28 cm
[4264]✳

134. Fragment of a composite textile of plain and tapestry weave in three strips with colours of red, yellow, white, brown, and black, to which have been sewn 12 rectangular silver plaques depicting zoomorphic figures in cut work. Yellow fringe. Chimu?
Overall H. 46 cm; overall W. 66 cm
[Unnumbered]

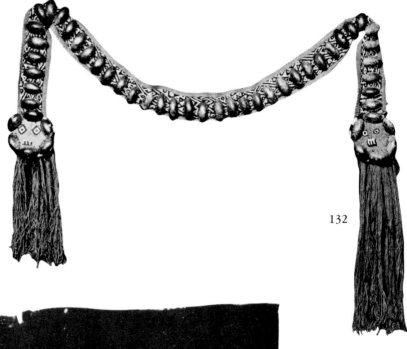

132

134

136

135. Mask. Resin with turquoise bead for pupil of eye. Two pendants beneath nose, and hemispherical disc appliqués on ear ornaments. Traces of red paint. Lambayeque style. Chimu.
H. 28.5 cm; W. 47.4 cm
[2060]✶

136. Poncho of small, scale-like, square plaques of gold sewn to a textile, one band of which is exposed and carries sixteen lozenge-shaped designs, each of which has a gold human mask at the centre. At the lower edge, discs are suspended from the textile. Probably resewn. Chimu?
L. 206 cm; W. 84 cm
[1906] Detail on cover.

137. Fragment of textile with rectangular gold plates still adhering. Chimu.
[Unnumbered]

138. *Tumi* profusely decorated with incised design on both faces. Square ornamented panels containing anthropomorphic figures are outlined with a wave design set off by stipple-chasing. Chimu.
L. 31.9 cm; greatest W. 13.7 cm
[3055]

139. Ornamental plaque decorated with cut-out and embossed birds, and geometric forms. Chimu.
H. 9.7 cm; W. 8.3 cm
[3086]

140. *Tumi.* Incised zoomorphic figures on handle and a human-face mask flanked by two birds on blade. Three bands of crow-step ornament. Lambayeque style. Chimu.
L. 13.7 cm; greatest W. 7.5 cm
[3082]

141. End plate of ear plug with anthropomorphic and zoomorphic figures and a border of radiating leaf ornament. Four staples for attaching to ear tube. Chimu.
Diam. 6.3 cm
[1840]

137

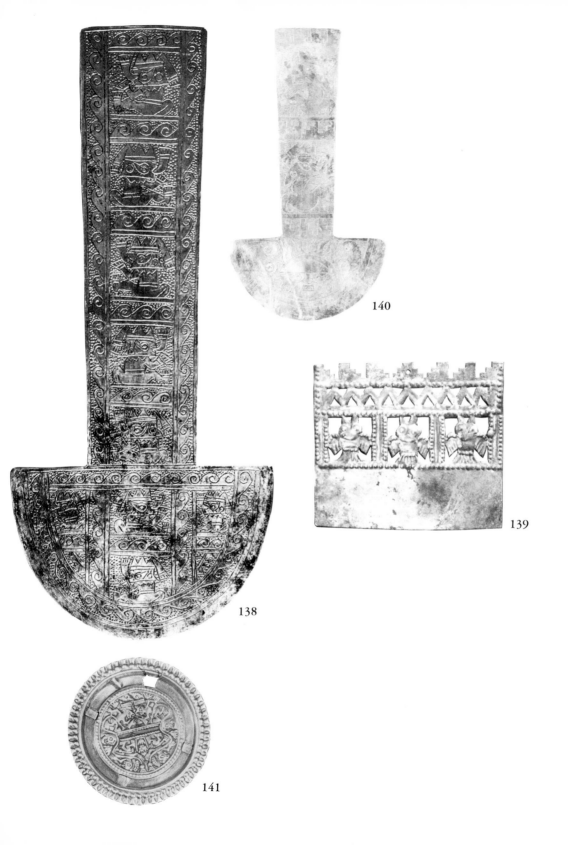

138

140

139

141

142. End plate of ear plug. In the central roundel is a divine (?) figure holding various plants (maize, yuca, and sweet potato); the remainder of the ground is divided into eight irregular sections depicting other figures bearing the same foodstuffs. Chimu.
Diam. 11.5 cm
[1828]

143. Mask. Features and ornament formed by embossing a single sheet. Bears traces of red and green paint. Lambayeque style. Chimu.
H. 37 cm; W. 64.1 cm
[1898]

144. Tall beaker with flaring sides and an embossed checkerboard pattern of stylized birds alternating with rectangles; the upper row of rectangles is set with four turquoises and one white chrysocolla. Upper and lower borders are of embossed wave pattern. Chimu.
H. 14.5 cm; Diam. of rim 9.6 cm
[4607]

145. Tall beaker with flaring sides and embossed with three standing figures holding staffs in panels separated and bordered at the top with crow-step designs. The figures have eyes upturned at the outer corners (Lambayeque style) and wear feather headdresses and decorated skirts. Chimu.
H. 20.5 cm; Diam. of rim 17 cm
[4589]

146. Tall beaker embossed with face and torso of a human figure with eyes in the Lambayeque style, ear ornaments, and a head-band; between the fingertips of the figure is a shell (?). Chimu.
H. 25.9 cm; Diam. of rim 20 cm
[4585]

147. Tall beaker with flat base, almost cylindrical but flaring sharply below rim. Decorated with a single band of embossed ornament, consisting of panels containing zoomorphic figures separated by vertical spacers of round bosses. Chimu.
H. 10 cm; Diam. of rim 9.8 cm
[4605]

148. Tall beaker with a double bottom and flaring sides, decorated with a wave pattern below the lip, a row of vertical rectangular depressions with beaded borders containing turquoise plaques, some with perforations, and a frieze of stylized birds. Three crosses are pierced in the lower wall of the vessel and one in the base. Chimu.
H. 13.2 cm; Diam. of rim 8 cm
[4608]✻

149. Ornament of embossed gold sheet in the form of a conch shell. Chimu?
L. 17.4 cm
[2904]

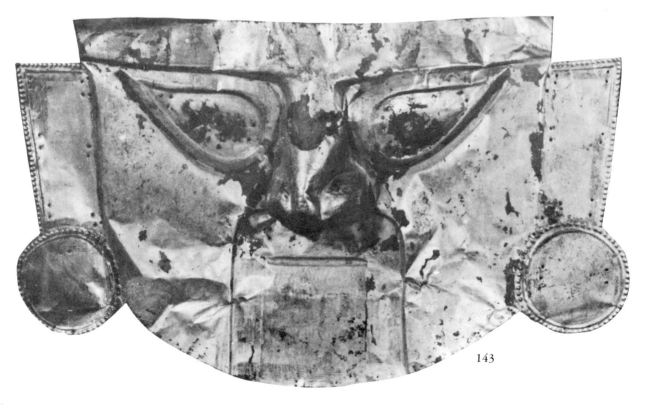

143

150. Ornamented gold sheets with square panels outlined with rows of large and small hemispherical bosses and, in two cases, with a wave pattern formed of small bosses. Now mounted to represent a ceremonial jacket or breastplate with two vertical panels, a horizontal panel to represent the yoke, and another to represent the belt. Traces of paint. Chimu?
H. (as mounted) 47.8 cm; W. 47 cm
[46]

151. Vessel in the form of a bird with a tall cylindrical and flaring spout in its back. Turquoise beads set in the eyes and gold bead suspended from the beak. Chimu?
L. 18.1 cm; H. 15.2 cm
[4631]

152. Vessel in the form of a parrot with a cylindrical flaring spout in its back. Wings and tail are made of separate sheets of embossed gold. Chimu.
L. 20 cm; H. 8.5 cm
[4634]✲

145

146

150

151

153

153. *Tumi.* Shaft is surmounted with an embossed seated anthropomorphic figure. Oval pendants hang from looped wires at the sides of the platform upon which the figure is seated. The domed headdress is decorated with a line of small bosses and surmounted by a crest in filigree, with a row of zigzag and a row of volute patterns. Three pieces of turquoise adorn the front of the headdress and circular turquoise ear ornaments depend from the ears. Three rectangular appendages protrude from the shoulders and side and a small *tumi* is held in the left hand. Lambayeque style. Chimu. H. 33.6 cm; W. 13.5 cm
[2443]

154, 155. A pair of roundels from ear ornaments. Within a plain border delimited by embossed beading is an openwork decoration of birds and crow-step designs. Chimu. Diam. 9.7 cm
[1821, 1822]

156. Tall beaker with flaring sides decorated with four standing figures. The eyes sweep upward at the outer corners in the Lambayeque style, and the ears have round ornaments; a crested domical headdress rests low on the forehead, and there appears to be a strap under the chin. A vertical band of triangles runs parallel to the upper arm on each side, and a similar band marks the bottom of the skirt (?). The legs and feet are bare. The frieze of figures is bordered top and bottom with a row of beading between raised lines. Chimu. H. 21 cm; Diam. of rim 17.5 cm
[4590]

154

157. Tall beaker with flaring sides decorated with two standing figures separated by vertical panels. Each figure has an elaborate domed headdress inset with turquoises, and plumes (?) spring from the sides. Turquoise beads are set in the ear ornaments. The outer corners of the eyes turn up in the Lambayeque style, and the mouth is hardened with vertical lines. A chin strap (?) to secure the helmet passes under the chin, and a breastplate is marked by embossing. The figures grasp tall staffs in extended arms and hands. Ornamental sashes (?) hang from the belt on either side. Crow-step designs fill the empty spaces around the figures, except between the legs. Below the lip of the cup runs a band of wave patterns bordered on either side by slightly raised margins. Chimu.
H. 20.5 cm; Diam. of rim 12 cm
[4591]

158. Tall beaker with flaring sides decorated simply with a broad, flat, embossed band around the middle. Chimu.
H. 17.3 cm; Diam. of mouth 10.6 cm
[4618]

159. Crown. A tall, waisted cylinder of sheet gold. Rows of horizontal bosses divide the crown into three bands, two of which are divided into rectangular panels by vertical rows of bosses. In alternating panels appear pairs of birds *en face,* their bodies represented by clusters of small bosses. The sheet gold of the crown is fastened with strap staples. Others probably held ornaments that extended above the crown. Chimu.
H. 19 cm
[3061]

160. Crown. A cylinder with a tall two-part plume, both of which are profusely decorated with circular bosses. Chimu.
Overall H. 38.2 cm; Diam. 17 cm
[3078]

160

156

159

161. Crown. A tall, waisted cylinder divided into three horizontal bands by double rows of small bosses. The upper and lower bands have rows of birds in relief. The broad central band has pairs of vertical zoomorphic figures in relief separated by triangles and diamonds; the background in all panels is covered with tiny random bosses. Chimu.
H. 19.5 cm; Diam. 19 cm
[2215]*

162. Double gold vessel. A beaker decorated with a simple embossed band below the rim is attached by a tube to a closed vessel representing two copulating animals adorned with turquoise beads, small bosses, and, in the case of one of them, a semi-circular crest. Chimu.
L. 24 cm; H. 16 cm
[4652]*

163. Tall beaker with flaring sides and a double base, set with 36 perforated turquoise or chrysocolla discs within beaded borders. Three crosses are pierced in the lower wall and one in the base. Chimu.
H. 13.8 cm; Diam. of rim 9.8 cm
[4601]

164. Gold sheet formed into a tube, presumably to cover a wooden baton or staff. Ornamented with three bands of animal figures and a small figure (of a bird?) mounted on a ring at one end. Chimu?
L. 17.3 cm; Diam. 1.8 cm
[1936]

165. Gold tube similar to 122, but with a bird (?) head at one end and a bird in the round at the other. Chimu?
L. 30.5 cm; Diam. 2.2 cm
[1922]

166. Gold tube similar to 123, but without the mounted bird in the round. Chimu?
L. 30.6 cm; Diam. 2 cm
[1931]

167, 168. Pair of discs from ear ornaments. A central turquoise or chrysocolla disc is surrounded by a band of stylized birds, cut out and embossed; the outer border is plain. Chimu.
Diam. 8.7 cm
[1811, 1812]

169, 170. Pair of discs from ear ornaments. A central turquoise or chrysocolla disc is surrounded by an openwork design of volutes in filigree and tiny balls; the outer border is plain. Chimu?
Diam. 7.9 cm
[1803, 1804]

171, 172. Pair of discs from ear ornaments. A central turquoise or chrysocolla disc is surrounded by an openwork design of volutes in filigree and tiny balls; the outer border is plain. Chimu?
Diam. 7.6 cm
[1805, 1806]

173, 174. Pair of discs from ear ornaments. A central boss is surrounded by a band of cut-out and embossed crow-step motifs; the outer border is plain. Chimu.
Diam. 10.1 cm
[1823, 1824]

175, 176. Pair of ear ornaments. The ornamental disc has a circular opening in the centre surrounded by a band of cut-out and embossed birds; the outer border is plain. Chimu.
Diam. 5.1 cm
[1997, 1998]

177, 178. Pair of ear ornaments. A central turquoise or chrysocolla disc is surrounded by an *ajouré* design of small gold balls soldered to concentric rings; the broad margin is of plain burnished gold. Chimu?
Diam. 7.7 cm
[Unnumbered, INC 155]

179, 180. Pair of ear ornaments. The disc bears a prominent central anthropomorphic figure with mask, crested headdress, and breastplate, flanked by two other figures. The tube is long and slender. Lambayeque style. Chimu.
L. 9.2 cm; Diam. 6.5 cm
[1969, 1970]

181. Small stylized anthropoid figure standing with hands clasped in front of the chest and a band across the forehead; bespangled with gold discs held by cut-wire clasps. Chimu.
H. 6.3 cm
[2433]

179

164

181

182. Tall beaker with flaring sides decorated with five bands of embossed ornament representing stylized birds and zoomorphic forms. Chimu.
H. 20.6 cm; Diam. of rim 9 cm
[4520]

183. Ceremonial *tumi,* the shaft terminating in a stylized deer standing on a base from which depend 12 elongated spangles. Chimu.
H. 30.5 cm
[3060]

184. Tall beaker with flaring sides, decorated with two broad bands of embossed waves, birds, and fish (?), bordered top and bottom with narrow bands of wave pattern. Chimu.
H. 18.9 cm
[4598]

185, 186. Pair of ceremonial gold hands and arms or gloves, with the fingers, thumbs, and the nails carefully depicted (the latter with applied silver). The arms are decorated with longitudinal bands containing embossed wave pattern, birds, scales, and triangles. On the backs of the hands are depicted files of warriors, in profile, with domed and plumed headdresses, breastplates, and short skirts. The eye form is in the Lambayeque style. Chimu.

> **185.** L. 53.9 cm
> [1902]✶
> **186.** L. 54.6 cm
> [1903]✶

187. "Tweezers" in axe form surmounted by a dog (?) with wire collar (?) supporting a pendant. Chimu.
H. 6 cm
[124]

183

184

188. "Tweezer" ornament in form of a bird with a crest. Chimu?
H. 3.9 cm
[184]

189. "Tweezer" ornament in form of a humming-bird in flight. Chimu?
L. 4.7 cm
[5235]

190. "Tweezer" ornament in form of a humming-bird in flight. Chimu?
L. 8.4 cm
[103]

191. "Tweezer" ornament in *tumi* form, the shaft ornamented with an embossed human face. Chimu?
H. 4.4 cm
[186]

192. "Tweezer" ornament in form of a humming-bird in flight. Chimu?
L. 8 cm
[4851]

193. "Tweezer" ornament with animal head and coiled tail. Chimu?
L. 5 cm
[4896]

194. "Tweezer" ornament bearing the representation of a helmeted head above which is a two-headed serpent. Lambayeque style. Chimu.
H. 4.6 cm; W. 3.8 cm
[177]

195. "Tweezer" ornament bearing the representation of a helmeted anthropomorphic figure holding a staff in each hand. Lambayeque style. Chimu.
H. 5.9 cm; W. 4.9 cm
[168]

196, 197. Pair of gold spindles, broadened in the middle and pierced with a hole; one end pointed, the other spatulate. Chimu?
   196. L. 17.5 cm
   197. L. 17.3 cm
   [2970, 2971]

198. Tall gold beaker with flaring sides and flat base. Ornament consists of a simple band of circular bosses between two raised lines. Chimu.
H. 14.5 cm; Diam. of rim 10.5 cm
[4648]

199. Tall gold beaker with flaring sides and flat base. The walls are ornamented with a checkerboard of plain squares alternating with squares embossed with stylized birds, bordered above and below with angular wave or crow-step pattern. Chimu.
H. 15.5 cm; Diam. of rim 10 cm
[4649]

199

121

200. Tall gold beaker with flaring sides
and flat base. Ornament consists of a simple
embossed band below the rim. Chimu.
H. 15.5 cm; Diam. of rim 10.3 cm
[4543]

201. Tall gold beaker with flaring sides
and flat base. Ornament consists of a band
of four embossed anthropomorphic heads
with domed headdresses and, below, a band
of four frogs. Chimu.
H. 14 cm; Diam. of rim 10.8 cm
[4639]

202. Tall gold beaker with flaring sides and
flat bottom. Ornament consists of two
anthropomorphic figures with ornate
headdresses, ear ornaments, and short skirts,
grasping two clubs or staffs with ornate
heads, and, below them, a band of stylized
birds. Lambayeque style. Chimu.
H. 15 cm; Diam. of rim 10.5 cm
[4517]

203. Tall gold rattle beaker with flaring
sides and flat base. The bottom is double
and has three crosses pierced in the lower
part. The ornament consists of two anthropomorphic figures with ornate headdresses,
ear ornaments, and short skirts, grasping
two clubs or staffs with ornate heads alternating with vertical bands of stylized birds.
Lambayeque syle. Chimu.
H. 14 cm; Diam. of rim 9.1 cm
[4521]

204. Tall gold beaker with flaring sides
and flat base. The ornament consists of 10
staff heads (?) in the shape of human heads
in profile with pyramid-shaped headdresses,
bordered above and below with crow-step
bands. Lambayeque style. Chimu.
H. 13 cm; Diam. of rim 9.5 cm
[4650]

205. Double-spouted, bridge-handled vase
of carinated form with flat base imitating
a common pottery shape. Stylized animal
heads, with protruding tongues, are attached
at the base of the spouts, and human-
headed beasts appear on shoulder and
bridge. The bridge is of openwork crested
with a crow-step pattern and surmounted
by a human head with ear spools and the
Lambayeque eye. Chimu.
H. 23 cm; W. 23.2 cm
[4630]*

203

208

207

206. Tall gold beaker with flaring sides and double bottom which contains three pierced crosses. Inlaid with three rectangular turquoises, one of which is crudely carved with a human face. Chimu.
H. 11.7 cm; Diam. of mouth 8.2 cm
[4612]

207. Gold pitcher with a globular body, high, flaring neck, and slightly pinched spout. One line of embossed ornament on shoulder. Chimu.
H. 13.4 cm; Diam. of mouth 7.8 cm
[4580]

208. Ear or nose ring. A double spiral of cut gold wire, in shell form with loop between. Chimu.
H. 2.5 cm; W. 3.5 cm
[351]

209-213. Five fingertip covers in shape of bird's head and beak; provided with holes for sewing to glove. Chimu.
[310-314]

214. Spoon or small cup with hemispherical bowl and flat, flaring handle. Chimu?
L. 11.5 cm
[346]

215, 216. "Tweezer" pendants with flat round heads and holes for sewing to a garment. Chimu.
L. 7 cm
[300, 301]

217. Feline in embossed gold. Chimu?
W. 8 cm
[293]

218. Necklace of shell, lapis lazuli, a mother-of-pearl disc, four gold spindles, two gold shells, a silver disc, a silver bell, and gold "tweezer" ornament, strung on the original braided cotton cord. Chimu?
L. 41 cm
[225]

219. Articulated gold bracelet of truncated cones fastened together with thread. Chimu?
[506]

214

217

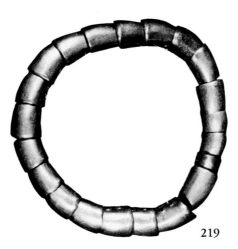

219

220. Gold mask, embossed. Green and white paint in eyes, below nose, and on ear ornament; pupils of eyes are gold hemispheres from which protrude thin gold tubes. Round and triangular spangles depend from ears and below nose. Forehead, nose, and mouth region highly burnished. Lambayeque style. Chimu.
H. 20.4 cm; W. 38.8 cm
[3076]

221. Small male figure carved in bone with turquoise and *Spondylus*-shell bead inlay. Chimu?
H. 6.2 cm; W. 2.6 cm
[1146]✳

220

222. Small female (?) figure carved in bone with turquoise-bead inlay and a headdress of natural quartz crystals. Chimu?
H. 7.1 cm; W. 2.5 cm
[1147]*

223. Gold funerary mask. Eyes of carved shell with copper pupils and protruding pointed wires. Disc-shaped ear ornaments with pendant bells; trapezoidal spangles hang from nostrils. Traces of white and green paint. Two halves of face joined with four metal staples; nose is separate; mask backed with plain weave cotton cloth. Lambayeque style. Chimu.
H. 31.1 cm; W. 43.3 cm
[1229]*

224, 225. Pair of circular ear ornaments, slightly concave; a central roundel, inlaid with a mosaic of turquoise, mother-of-pearl, lapis lazuli, red *Spondylus* shell, and jade (?) within a plain surround of shell bordered with gold beads. Chimu.
Diam. 6.8 cm
[1884, 1885]

226. One of a pair of ceremonial digging staffs. Embossed sheet gold over wood, shod with heavy forged copper digging point. Lozenge-shaped head is ornamented with eight stylized human figures, in four facing pairs; domical headdresses with flaring plumes. Behind each figure is a lizard(?). Below this frieze is a "swimming" man with a long curved tongue and wearing a crown. The swelling at the base of the head of the staff represents a human mask with Lambayeque eyes, large round ear ornaments, and a domical headdress with plumes on either side. The upper part of the shaft, a long gold tube nailed to a wooden core with bronze nails, is embossed with diagonal bands of stylized and geometric forms. Lambayeque style. Chimu.
L. 247 cm
[1896]*

224-225

226

227. *Tumi.* A ceremonial knife with blade and shaft of silver, alternating sections of which are overlaid with gold foil to create checkerboard effect. Finial is an anthropomorphic head with turquoise-bead eyes, and ear spools and pendant earrings of gold turquoise. Headdress inset with turquoise roundels and red *Spondylus* shell, above which rises a filigree crest which supports, on either side, a pendant bird inlaid with turquoise and holding a lapis lazuli bead on a gold ring in its beak. Lambayeque style. Chimu.
H. 27.7 cm; W. 10.3 cm
[2708]✳

228. Crown. A tall cylindrical headdress of thin sheet gold with five rows of flat bell-shaped pendants supported by cut wire. Top row also has two embossed anthropomorphic heads which originally had small flat pendants (one remaining) below the chin; traces of white paint on masks. Lambayeque style. Chimu.
H. 22 cm; Diam. 20 cm
[2881]

229. Small sheet-gold anthropomorphic figure holding tiny jade (?) beads aloft and wearing a domical headdress surmounted by a crest; red paint on face. Lambayeque style. Chimu.
H. 4.6 cm; W. 4 cm
[2837]

228

230

126

230. Fan-shaped sheet of gold, embossed, with four radiating panels, each subdivided into four sections bearing depictions of anthropomorphic figures, usually in pairs standing back to back, holding serpents by the neck or grasping long staffs with ornate finials. Possibly an agricultural rite. Chimu. H. 11.5 cm; greatest W. 18 cm
[2715]

231. Gold crest (?). Embossed gold and cut-out pattern of animals with protruding tongues. Gold staples around inner edge presumably once secured it to some other element now missing (compare 244). Chimu?
Greatest W. 34 cm; breadth of band 5.3 cm
[2714]

232. Figurine formed of a flat piece of mother-of-pearl (strengthened with wood behind head), carved and incised with human features, and provided with turquoise-bead eyes, a gold-foil cap (bearing an anthropomorphic face), and bands around the arms. Chimu.
H. 8 cm
[2910]

229

232

231

127

236

233. Tiny embossed figure of a warrior carrying a club or staff and wearing a helmet with a high crest. Chimu.
H. 4 cm
[2999]✷

234. *Tumi.* Ceremonial knife with blade and shaft of silver, the former completely overlaid and the latter partly overlaid in checkerboard fashion with gold foil. Finial consists of two animals in the round with red *Spondylus*-bead inserts for eyes and circular turquoise-bead inlays in ears, on the body, and on the rectangular base. Two gold quatrefoil blossoms hang from the neck of each animal. Chimu.
H. 27.5 cm; W. of blade 11 cm
[3059]✷

235. Crown. A composite headdress consisting of a cylindrical, slightly waisted element to which are attached five separate decorative elements:
(1) Across the front, a flat sheet narrower in the centre and flaring at both ends.
(2) Above (1) rises a high flat sheet with horizontal lower edge and sides curving upward to a rounded top.
(3-5) Three sheets similar to (2) in the form of a reversed *tumi* (compare 244). All five elements are covered with pendant, shallow, dish-shaped discs, secured with gold staples. Around the borders of all five sheets is secured (with copper staples) a plain band of copper (or silver with green patina), except on the straight, vertical sides of elements 3-5, where the border consists of stylized animals in cut copper (or silver); the whole band shows traces of having once been covered with coloured cotton-wool or down. The absence of clamps or other mechanical means of securing the five flat elements to the central cylindrical headdress suggests strongly that the present reconstruction is hypothetical, but the several parts may be Chimu.
Total H. as mounted 55.6 cm; H. of central cylinder 19.8 cm; greatest Diam. 18.8 cm
[1651]

235

236. Breastplate. Gold and copper plaques fastened like scales to a textile backing, and bordered at the bottom with pendant beads and metal ornaments. At the shoulders there are two *tumi* plaques which have embossed human faces and elaborate headdresses. Chimu.
H. (without pendants) 34 cm; W. 34.5 cm
[3720]

237. Back-rest of litter, made of a plank of wood *(algorrobo* [?], a type of acacia). As originally used, the decorated side would be to the rear, where it would be seen; the plain side, simply painted in brown and cream, was presumably once covered by a textile pad or pillow (remains of cotton twine support this view, as does the litter model of 250), as was the floor. The ornamented side bears six large portals and two small double portals (that is, they could be seen from front and rear) richly decorated with gold, paint, metal pendants, and possibly feathers. All portals except the two smaller ones contain three figures, fully caparisoned in gold headdresses, masks, breastplates, etc., of types seen elsewhere in the exhibition. The central figure in each case is slightly recessed, stands on a low platform, and is more richly dressed. Solitary figures stand between the portals in the upper row and in the smaller double portals to either side below. Said to have been found at Chan Chan. Lambayeque style. Chimu.
H. of back-rest 58 cm; W. 113.5 cm; Th. 8 cm diminishing to 2.0 — 3.5 cm at edges. Support rods (for securing the back-rest to the horizontal poles carried on the shoulders of attendants) are 128 cm and 120 cm in length.
[4059]*

237

239

243

238. Child's poncho formed of two separately woven pieces of light ochre cotton material sewn together in the centre and on the sides, leaving 6-cm openings for the arms. The vertical neck opening is 16 cm long. A separate band, in tapestry weave, forms a border. The ground fabric is covered with cut-out geometric and wave patterns in gold foil, with interspersed embossed masks, birds, and discs; some of the gold is burnished, some matt. The arrangement of goldwork is hypothetical. As now constituted, the front of the garment is more richly ornamented with gold than the back. Chimu.
L. of garment (opened out) 61 cm;
W. 49.5 cm
[4114]*

239. Cap, domed, with flattened top consisting of heavy cord over reed supports. To this base is sewn a pattern of four small gold squares alternating with larger embossed silver squares on the sides, and eight of the latter on top. In front, a symmetrical cut-out and embossed ornament in gold foil. Eight projecting wires around top edge bear lunate pendants, four of which have embossed masks, and at the front there is a "plume" of cut-out gold foil. Lower border of cap has a band of small rectangular sheet plaques with pendants. Chimu?
H. 14.5 cm; Diam. 23 cm
[4151]

240. Head-band (?) formed of shell segments in a variety of colours and cut in geometric shapes which fit together. The segments are strung on two parallel strings which terminate in tubular woven red cords, and are mounted on a very poorly preserved textile. Chimu.
L. (shell only) 34 cm; (with cords) 49 cm;
W. 4.6 cm
[4162]

241, 242. Two jar-shaped finials, formed by embossing and grooving. Chimu?
Hs. ca. 3.5 cm
[5229, 5230]

243. Wooden box. Lid, apparently originally hinged with cord, is decorated with two square panels containing figures wearing domed headdresses, plumes reaching to the ground, breastplates, and short skirts. They are framed in geometric patterns which also cover the other sides and ends, inset with gold and silver sheet, mother-of-pearl, and shell. Lambayeque style. Chimu.
L. 23.4 cm; H. 9.9 cm; W. 11.9 cm
[4271]

244. Standard (?) or part of a crown (?) in the form of a tree with four branches on either side terminating in stylized animal heads; an upper fan-shaped crest is bordered with gold, embossed and stapled on. From the branches, and within circular holes cut in the upper portion, depend gold drops in oval or disc form. The "trunk" and "branches" show evidence of having once been completely covered with some substance (dyed cotton-wool?) secured with very fine thread. (Compare with two side and rear panels of made-up crown, 235). Chimu.
H. 32.3 cm
[2897]*

245. Drinking vessel with double bottom, in the form of a human leg and foot. Constructed of five pieces, three gold, two silver; the drinking portion proper is made up of two gold sections and one silver, raised by hammering (like the beakers and jars elsewhere in the exhibition), shaped to the leg form, and apparently soldered together. The foot, of silver, is embossed and provided with five gold toenails clamped on. The gold sole of the foot, embossed and grooved to represent the underside of the toes, is secured to the upper part with clamps. Chimu.
H. 19 cm
[4703]*

246. Ornamental disc of silver, possibly the cover of a shield of leather or woven cane, with a central boss and four concentric bands of intricate embossed designs:
(1) Innermost: stylized animals with human heads wearing headdresses, and tails ending in fish (?) with heads and fins; between the animals are monkeys.
(2) Man walking to the left and, behind him, a monkey whose tail forms a meander all round the panel and terminates in a tassel. Behind the tail are other figures, possibly monkeys, walking to the right, and other small indistinct motifs, of which one is a bird.
(3) Repeated designs of human masks with dome headdresses, "cornucopia" forms with protruding plumes, and fish, separated by S-shaped embossed lines crossing the band diagonally.
(4) Outermost: a wider band contains a repeat design of a reed (tortora) boat with a high ornamented stem and a square stern, carrying two men with paddles and a piled-up net (?). In front of the boat are two ducks (?) and two tortora fronds (?). Behind the boat (in the water) are two other (human?) figures, one in profile, one en face, swimming (?). Chimu.
Diam. 34.8 cm
[4841]

247. Poncho made of two similar pieces of tapestry-weave textile sewn together, leaving an opening for the head. Against this yellow-ochre background there is a brocaded zigzag pattern with enrichment in a variety of colours. The lower edges are hung with embossed bell-shaped gold plaques, and gold ornaments in other forms are spread in roughly symmetrical arrangement over the whole textile. To some of these gold plaques blue paint still adheres. Chancay.
L. of garment (opened out) 106 cm; W. (without fringes) 86 cm
[4130]

247

246

133

248, 249. Pair of child's boots, made of two pieces of red tapestry-woven material, L-shaped, lined with cotton tabby, to which are sewn square gold plates. A single gold sheet, cut out in the shape of five toes, and with grooves marking toenails, is sewn to each boot. Chancay.
L. 13.5 cm; H. 12.5 cm; W. 7 cm
[4143, 4144]*

250. Miniature funerary procession, together with other grave goods, in gold, silver, and copper.
(1) A litter consisting of two longitudinal poles, two flat cross-members, and the flat floor of the seat. Two additional cross-pieces are lashed to the poles, the rear one bound, in turn, to the sloping back-rest. The front side of this panel, against which the rider would recline, is plain and is provided with a "cushion". This and the mat on the floor, by means of embossing, simulate textiles with wave designs. The rear side of the back-rest, which would be visible to onlookers, has an embossed design of birds (?). The litter is carried by four men; it is empty and we are to understand, presumably, that the owner is the departed represented in (2).
L. of litter 22 cm; W. 10.5 cm
(2) Two figures similar to the litter bearers carry a long pole to which is lashed a long oval object, which probably contains the mummy bundle of the deceased. The lead bearer appears also to hold a bell or rattle.
(3) A sun-shade consists of a vertical pole and a square sun-shield with feather ornaments hanging at each corner and a vase-shaped finial containing (as displayed) a "bouquet" of yellow feathers.
(4) A four-legged platform, the square top of which has a low "balustrade". On one side, a metal representation of a portal similar to those on the back-rest (237).
(5) Four ornamental poles of tubular metal, two with jar-shaped finials, two with simple, flaring openings. As displayed, they contain yellow feathers, and may represent *torchères.*

(6) A small square plaque on which are mounted a seated (?) human figure holding a jar in which there is a rod with an ornamental head, and a standing figure with an embossed mask, ear ornaments, a gold head-band, and a headdress of blue feathers.
(7) A square plaque with upturned sides contains five trees or plants bearing fruits, pods, etc. The pattern on the bottom of the plaque probably represents furrows and the upturned sides may be the heaped-up earth borders of the irrigated fields.
(8) A flat "mat" with an embossed crow-step pattern bears (as displayed) 22 representations of beans, in pods or shelled.
(9) A long oval sheet with embossed round depressions carries (as displayed) 17 or 18 representations of fish and shellfish.
(10) A reed boat, a bird standing on its stem-post, and a paddle.
(11) A large variety of individual miniatures: *tumis,* garment pins, vessels and receptacles (beakers, jars, pans), instruments (flutes, pan-pipes), etc.
It is presumed that all these miniatures represent the household goods, food and drink, and other possessions of the deceased noble, provided for his use in the other world. However, the disparity in size and materials of the objects suggests that not all are from one tomb. Silver pieces Chancay (from Lauri).
[4286]

251. Feather poncho of two contrasting colours, blue and yellow, on front and back, the feathers secured to an original off-white textile backing. The shoulder section, now without feathers, probably once had them, for the traces of stitching are still evident. The neck slit and the shoulder section are now outlined by embossed gold birds (20) and pendant discs (12), but this may be a hypothetical reconstruction. Chancay.
L. (opened out) 200 cm; W. 71 cm
[4355]

252. Feather headdress of waisted cylindrical form, bordered top and bottom by metal bands. The feathers are arranged in a checkerboard design of dark red, yellow, light blue, and violet; from the top, all round, projects a stiff plume of vertical yellow feathers. Chancay.
H. 28 cm; Diam. 14.7 cm
[4360]*

253. T-shaped sheet with stylized human face. Inca.
H. 14.8 cm; W. 15.4 cm
[1139]

254. Mask with stylized human face bordered by serpents. Inca?
H. 22 cm; W. 25 cm
[1232]*

255, 256. Pair of ornaments consisting of one flat and one slightly conical element, the former having an embossed border. Inca?
Diam. of flat disc 4.1 cm
[3162, 3163]

257, 258. Pair of shawl pins with disc heads, undecorated. Inca.
L. 36.3 cm
[3140, 3141]

259. Jar with vertical strap handles, tall cylindrical neck, flat projecting rim and flat base. Inca.
H. 10.5 cm
[4670]

259

250(1) Artist's impression from photograph

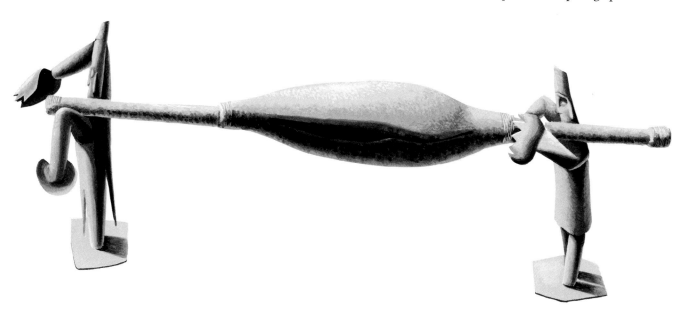

250(2) Artist's impression from photograph

260

260, 261. Pair of tall beakers with flaring sides and flat everted rim. Below the rim, and outlined with raised bands, six stylized human faces with rectangular mouths containing prominent teeth. Inca?
H. 6.5 cm; Outer diam. of rim 6.2 cm
[4667, 4671]

262, 263. Pair of "wrist guards" or mounts from wooden staffs. The sheets were joined together in tubular form with clamps or staples through the matching pairs of holes along the edges. Inca?
L. 20 cm
[3147, 3148]

264. Small figure of a lame male clasping a crutch in both hands. Inca.
H. 3.6 cm
[3218]*

265-268. Small figures, three female and one male, standing with hands resting on their breasts (in a worshipping attitude?). Inca.
H. 6.2 cm
[3212, 3206, 3204, 3213]*

269. Gold stylized llama. Inca.
H. 2.5 cm; L. 2.4 cm
[3224]

270. Balance beam and pans. The beam is copper (?) cast by *cire perdue* process (?). An upper cresting of crow-step pattern, with two end verticals, encloses a border of balls. Within this, an S-spiral motif outlines two square openings which contain parrots (?), their wings and tails stylized but their heads in the round, protruding. From either end of the beam are suspended gold pans. The cords and knots may all be original. Inca?
H. of balance beam 4.7 cm; W. 6.8 cm
[3311]

271. Mace. The double head, with two rows of eight protruding spikes, is probably gold over a silver/copper alloy. The wooden shaft (a replacement) is covered with sheet gold, the surface of which has a heavy encrustation of copper corrosion products. Original association of head and shaft not demonstrable. Head is Inca.
L. 84.5 cm
[2054]*

272-281. Ten gold rings of various forms. Chimu and Vicus.
Diams. 1.7–2.3 cm
[364, 361, 357, 356, 4812, 4813, 363, 4814, 4816, 4815]

282. Girdle. Three strands of hollow gold beads support 35 vertical elements consisting of two or three tubular beads embossed with human faces and geometric forms and terminating in spherical beads. Traces of red paint appear on some beads. Restrung.
L. 84.2 cm; W. 7 cm
[3073]

283. Necklace of jar-shaped beads separated by pairs of spherical beads. Restrung.
L. 125 cm
[1615]

284. Necklace of spherical beads and bells. Restrung.
L. 152 cm
[1640]

285. Necklace of gold rings. Restrung.
L. 77 cm
[5355]

286. Necklace of spherical bells separated by pairs of beads. Restrung.
L. 102 cm
[1614]

287. Necklace of hollow beads. Restrung.
L. 97 cm
[2050]

288. Necklace of large and small spherical beads with "tweezer" pendant. Restrung.
L. 147.2 cm
[2078]

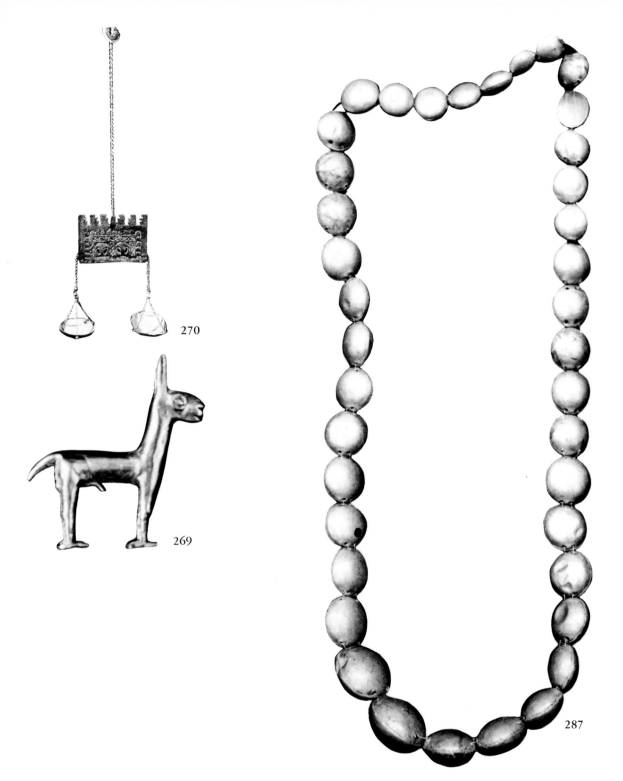

270

269

287

289. Collar consisting of three strands of spherical beads separated by two strands of lentoid beads; pendants of similar beads. Restrung.
L. 50 cm
[3315]

290. Necklace of lentoid and large and small spherical beads. Restrung.
L. 168 cm
[1639]

291. Collar consisting of "tweezer" elements pendant from a strand of spherical beads. Restrung.
L. 79 cm
[2061]

292. Necklace of gold tubes and hollow round beads of three sizes. Restrung.
L. 183 cm
[2041]

293. Necklace. A double strand made of graduated hollow beads in the form of fish vertebrae. Restrung.
L. 134 cm
[2049]

294. Necklace. Multiple strands of hollow beads bound together by three transverse bands. Restrung.
L. 68 cm
[2063]

295. Necklace of spherical and drum-shaped hollow beads; the pendant has a turquoise tubular bead and a "tweezer" ornament. Restrung.
L. 100.7 cm
[857]

296. Necklace of alternating pearls and spherical gold beads. Restrung.
L. 54 cm
[829]

297. Composite necklace of spherical gold beads, turquoise beads, and one tiny representation of a human head; the pendant is a double strand of hollow gold frogs and fish vertebrae terminating in a hollow bead with a human face. Restrung.
L. 90 cm
[870]

291

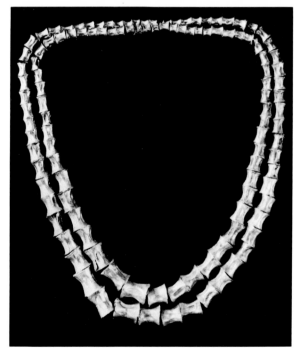

293

138

298. Composite necklace of spherical gold and red *Spondylus*-shell beads with a crescent and a "tweezer" pendant. Restrung. L. 128 cm [871]

299. Composite necklace of spherical gold, red *Spondylus* shell, and tubular stone beads. Restrung. L. 170 cm [823]

300. Necklace of tubular beads. Restrung. L. 249 cm [2068]

301. Necklace. Irregularly shaped beads of turquoise and hollow gold beads support a double strand of five large, hollow, cushion-shaped gold beads. Restrung. L. 66 cm [1344]

302. Necklace. Beads consist of rock crystal, emeralds, and gold. Restrung. L. 93 cm [1368]

303. Necklace. Two strands of beads, one of turquoises, the other of lapis lazuli interspersed with tubular gold beads, from which hangs a pendant consisting of hollow gold beads, one turquoise, and one lapis lazuli bead. Restrung. L. 86 cm [3688]

304. Necklace. A string of hollow gold beads carries eight lappets or pendants consisting of embossed human heads with domed headdresses and deep collars inlaid with turquoise beads; a larger central pendant has the form of a human-headed gold bird in which turquoise beads and larger, irregular pieces of turquoise are set. Below this hang three drops, each consisting of roughly oval pieces of turquoise in beaded frames. Restrung. Pendants are Lambayeque style. L. 71 cm [464]✷

301

139

317

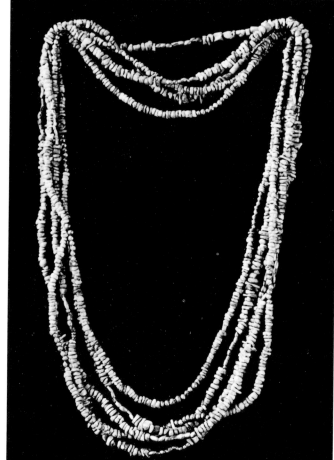

322

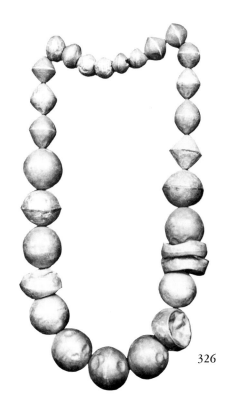

326

140

305. Necklace of hollow beads interspersed with pendant baroque pearls (42 pearls, 42 large gold beads). Restrung.
L. 58 cm
[1378]

306. Necklace of rock-crystal beads and a rectangular rock-crystal pendant. The beads have been drilled in a biconical form. Restrung.
L. 94 cm
[4917]

307. Necklace of 47 biconical gold beads separated by pairs of turquoise beads and one carnelian (?) bead. Restrung.
L. 96 cm
[1768]

308. Necklace consisting of oval gold beads, shell beads, and incised spindle whorls. Pendant consists of incised black stones. Restrung.
L. 163 cm
[1359]

309. Necklace of tubular and spherical rock-crystal beads separated by hollow gold beads and two green stones (emeralds?). The central pendant is a rock-crystal ball. The rock-crystal beads have been drilled in biconical form. Restrung.
L. 86 cm
[1355]

310. Necklace of rock-crystal, lapis lazuli, turquoise, amethyst (rose quartz?), carnelian, emerald, and gold beads. The pendant is a rough piece of turquoise (chrysocolla). Restrung.
L. 90 cm
[2085]

311. Necklace. Beads of various forms and materials — rose quartz, turquoise, lapis lazuli — together with gold balls. Restrung.
L. 158 cm
[1341]

312. Necklace of turquoise beads in a variety of shapes and sizes, supporting eight frog's heads in gold which, in turn, are connected by a looping string of beads on which is suspended a central human figure and two side human heads in gold. Restrung.
L. 81 cm
[1391]

313. Necklace of 13 strands of tiny gold tubular beads. Restrung.
L. 108 cm
[Unnumbered INC 330]

314. Necklace. Spherical and oblate gold beads with cabochon gems (topaz?). Restrung.
L. 86 cm
[1373]

315. Necklace. Gold beads with rock crystal, rose quartz, turquoise, carnelian, and amethyst. Restrung.
L. 77 cm
[1370]

316. Necklace. Gold beads with turquoise, amethyst, and rock crystal. Restrung.
L. 122 cm
[1362]

317. Necklace of small gold beads and nine hollow anthropomorphic figures with round eyes and hands on their chests. Restrung.
L. 11 cm
[1351]

318. Necklace of spherical gold beads alternating with "tweezer" pendants. Restrung.
L. 85 cm
[1619]

319. Necklace of tubular and round turquoise beads alternating with gold beads; the pendant contains a long malachite (?) bead. Restrung.
L. 136 cm
[1340]

320. Necklace of embossed gold beads alternating with emeralds; the pendant consists of gold beads and a large clear emerald. Restrung.
L. 70.5 cm
[1367]

321. Necklace of tubular rose quartz beads alternating with gold balls; the pendant contains turquoise. Restrung.
L. 66.5 cm
[4942]

322. Necklace of turquoise and tiny gold beads. Restrung.
L. 362 cm
[3689]

323. Necklace. Twelve large, hollow gold balls formed from soldered hemispheres. Restrung.
L. 62 cm
[1628]

324. Necklace. A strand of 39 hollow gold balls, graduated in size, with three tubular and two rhomboidal beads, from which hangs a pendant of gold beads of various shapes, terminating in a "tweezer" ornament embossed with two intertwined serpents. Restrung.
L. 135 cm
[2065]

325. Necklace. Composed of multicoloured shell and gold beads. Restrung.
L. 71 cm
[1050]

326. Necklace. Gold spheres of various sizes, some of which have been flattened or otherwise damaged. Restrung.
L. 92 cm
[2071]

327. Necklace containing turquoise beads, gold spherical beads (some embossed), and supporting a pendant of gold balls, two triple ball forms (soldered together), and a rhomboid finial. Restrung.
L. 140 cm
[434]

328. Necklace of gold balls and chrysocolla tubular beads supporting a pendant consisting of two tiny vase forms, one in gold, the other in chrysocolla. Restrung.
L. 98 cm
[468]

329. Necklace of tiny gold balls, gold snails, and hollow beads with human features, together with turquoise beads. A short strand connects the lower portions of the main strand and consists of gold balls and a single turquoise bead. Restrung.
L. 107 cm
[239]

330. Necklace of turquoise and hollow gold beads with a rectangular pendant made up of a mosaic of red shell, mother-of-pearl, and turquoise. Restrung.
L. 77 cm
[1029]

331. Necklace of tiny tubular silver beads and emeralds with a turquoise carved in human form as a pendant. Restrung.
L. 110 cm
[1032]

332. Necklace composed of 24 tiny representations of owls separated by four gold balls in a double row. Restrung.
L. 68 cm
[4850]

333. Necklace. Composed of tubular beads of chrysocolla, round beads of rock crystal, four shell plaques, and gold balls, with a pendant of white shell inlaid with tiny coral beads. Restrung.
L. 94 cm
[1052]

334. Necklace. Turquoise beads of various forms and one embossed tubular gold bead. Restrung.
L. 67 cm
[38]

335. Necklace. Gold chestnut-coloured resin beads alternating and of graduated size. Restrung.
L. 150 cm
[15]

336. Necklace. Three strands of multi-coloured shell beads support a central ornament of chrysocolla beads terminating in a gold pendant, while five similar gold pendants flank it on either side. Restrung.
L. 80 cm
[460]

337. Necklace. Sixteen flat pieces of chrysocolla are supported by a triple strand of turquoise and gold beads. Restrung.
L. 64 cm
[1054]

338. Necklace. Four interwoven strands of gold and turquoise beads with gold-bead pendants as a fringe on outer strand. Restrung.
L. 60 cm
[844]

339. Necklace. Four strands of gold and pearl beads with a pendant composed of a pearl, an emerald, and four gold beads. Restrung.
L. 77 cm
[1059]

340. Necklace. A strand of gold balls with eight larger gold beads embossed, and one chrysocolla bead carved, with human faces; from these depend drops of alternating gold and turquoise beads, and they are connected with loops of small gold balls. Restrung.
L. 80 cm
[1057]

341. Necklace. Rose quartz, turquoise, and gold beads of various sizes and shapes support a pendant carved with a zoomorphic face. Restrung.
L. 80 cm
[1069]

342. Necklace. Four strands of gold beads of round and ellipsoidal form terminate in eight tubular chrysocolla beads and a central chrysocolla figure. Restrung.
L. 60 cm
[1055]

343. Necklace. Four strands of small gold balls and ellipsoidal beads terminating in a small figurine of turquoise with coral beads for eyes. Restrung.
L. 62 cm
[1066]

344. Necklace. Gold and turquoise beads of various shapes and sizes (and one of coal) roughly graduated. Restrung.
L. 76 cm
[4]

345. Necklace. A strand of spherical gold and tubular turquoise beads supports four pendants which have quatrefoil blossom and "tweezer" elements. Restrung.
L. 103 cm
[37]

346. Necklace. Hollow gold beads of fish-vertebra and human-head forms support a pendant consisting of two irregularly shaped chrysocollas and a gold bead in the form of a human head. Restrung.
L. 68.2 cm
[243]

347. Necklace. A main strand of spherical gold beads alternating with discs of coral supports a loop and three pendants of gold fish-vertebra-shaped beads, terminating in a central "tweezer" ornament shaped like a bird and two others of roughly oval form. Restrung.
L. 81.3 cm
[839]

348. Necklace. A strand of embossed gold tubular beads supports a pendant terminating in a tiny anthropomorphic figure. Restrung.
L. 135 cm
[454]

349. Necklace. A strand of shell beads supports gold cones and openwork silver bells with anthropomorphic features. Restrung.
L. 108 cm
[433]

350. Necklace. A strand of small shell beads with gold conch shells and curved shell leaves. Restrung.
L. 93 cm
[461]

351. Necklace. Gold beads of various forms and a pendant disc with an embossed geometric ornament. Restrung.
L. 98 cm
[36]

347

352. Necklace. A strand of gold double beads alternating with turquoise discs supports a pendant terminating in a hunchbacked anthropoid figure. Restrung.
L. 106.5 cm
[845]

353. Necklace. Tubular beads of lapis lazuli — some round, some square, some hexagonal in section — alternate with hollow gold beads. Restrung.
L. 88 cm
[877]

354. Necklace. Groups of small silver tubular beads alternate with groups of red shell discs and support a silver disc with wave, crow-step, and bird design. Restrung. The disc may be Chimu.
L. 46.5 cm; Diam. of disc 10.1 cm
[73]

355. Necklace. Spherical gold beads alternate with discs of jade (?), yellow and red shell, and jet. Restrung.
[9]

356. Necklace. Two strands of coral-coloured shell beads linked at intervals and supporting a variety of pendants: embossed gold hat shapes, birds, cones, etc. Restrung.
[236]

357. Circular collar of overlapping rows of rectangular, triangular, and circular mother-of-pearl plaques, each row of plaques having a spherical gold bead. Restrung.
Diam. 38 cm
[245]

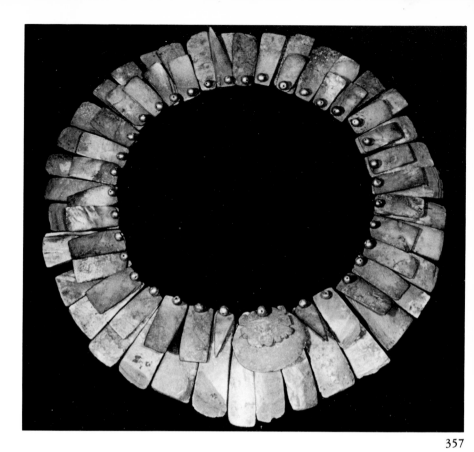

357

359

360

358. Necklace of minute red *Spondylus* and black stone (?) beads. Restrung. [794]

359. Necklace of delicate gold tubes and two turquoise beads. The pendant is a coastal Chavin-style zoomorphic figure incised on stone. Restrung. [824]

360. Collar of 17 pendants, each consisting of small turquoise beads *pavé*, in gold-wire and ball frames, and suspended from a strand of spherical gold beads. Restrung. [848]

361. Deep collar consisting of six concentric elements: an inner row of double, barrel-shaped stone beads; four rows of fish forms in carved stone and shell inlaid with turquoise, *Spondylus* shell, and other materials, interspersed with globular and tubular gold and silver beads; an outer row representing fish heads (?), which also outline the opening of the collar at the back where gold hooks provide a means of fastening the collar in place. Restrung. [1060]

362. Bronze mould section for making a monkey (?) mask, with a boss on the reverse. Inca?
L. 4.3 cm; greatest W. 5 cm; greatest Th. (without boss) 2.6 cm
[1198]

363. Broken stone mould of very fine-grained dark grey stone. A rosette of six petals, surrounded with a line of rope pattern, is incised on one side and a similar, but smaller, rosette, with eight petals, on the reverse. Colonial period?
L. 9 cm; Diam. of larger rosette 4.6 cm; Diam. of smaller rosette 3 cm
[1207]

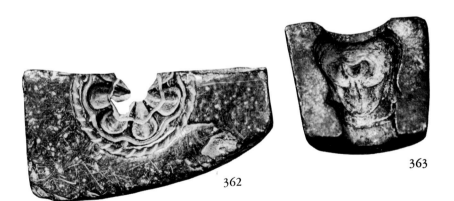

362

363

364. Breastplate of slightly curved metal to which is attached, with staples, a central embossed, seated figure with crossed legs and with hands resting on knees. The figure wears a domed headdress ornamented on top with square and round plaques and terminating on the sides in large hemispherical attachments. The ears support ear ornaments, while a plain necklace with a round bauble hangs on the bare chest. A belt with a central zone of intersecting lines is at the waist, and the upper arms and shoulders are covered with a short sleeve or mantle. The remainder of the breastplate is covered with pendants attached by staples. The surface is heavily covered with copper corrosion products, but gold is present. Some red paint is also visible. Holes on either side of the centre at top presumably were used to secure the breastplate. For further comments see 365.
H. 27.4 cm; W. 34.7 cm
[128]

365. Breastplate similar to 364, but the central figure is running, brandishing a rectangular shield in its right hand, a club in its left. The arms have wristlets and the legs anklets. The domed headdress, which has side-pieces descending to the shoulders, supports a crescent-shaped crest. A necklace of large balls supports a mask (?) in the centre of the chest. The belt has three rectangular zones with central bosses. Above the knees there are decorated bands, but it is not clear whether these are ornaments or fringes of a garment. Surface like 364. Holes at the outer, upper corners were presumably used for suspension.
H. 28 cm; W. 33.6 cm
[133]

The faces of the figures represented on 364 and 365 are completely unlike anything seen elsewhere in Peruvian collections. They are round, with broad and full cheeks; the eyes are lozenge-shaped with round pupils, and eyebrows are well defined; the mouth is recessed but the lips are full above a small chin. The possibility must be considered that these breastplates come from outside Peru.

364

365